MINES TO
MEDICINE

JUDGE MYLES O'CONNOR

MINES TO
MEDICINE

*The Exciting Years of Judge Myles O'Connor,
His Hospital and the Pioneer Physicians
of the Santa Clara Valley*

By DANIEL D. HRUBY

San José, California
1965

Published by

O'CONNOR HOSPITAL
2105 Forest Avenue
San Jose, California 95128

Cover Design by Eugene J. Rossi

Lithographed and bound in U. S. A. by Rosicrucian Press, Ltd., San Jose, California

CONTENTS

Dedicated

To Sister Roberta

of the Daughters of Charity

of St. Vincent de Paul

Foreword

This is a book about medicine in the Santa Clara Valley of California—how it started and how it developed.

It is told mostly through the life of a man who unwittingly played a significant role in the nascent years, Myles Poore O'Connor. An Irish emigrant, he joined the forty-niners and drove a mule team over the rocky Overland Trail to California. Bent on the practice of law, he was sidetracked by the rush for gold.

Out of those turbulent years, O'Connor built a fortune—a fortune he considered a sacred trust. He was 61 years old when he moved to San José from Grass Valley and the Sierra Nevada mining country. At such an age, most men think only of retrenchment and retirement. Yet over the next 25 years O'Connor and his wife, Amanda, made their finest contributions to society as they drew upon their fortune to comfort the suffering and inspire hope in the despairing.

Even today, it is difficult to travel anywhere in the Santa Clara Valley and be out of sight of some edifice that does not owe its existence or development to Myles O'Connor.

Lawyer, gold miner, justice of the peace, legislator, world traveler and philanthropist, O'Connor was a man of infinite compassion. His concern for the orphaned and the elderly led to the construction of a sanitarium. A community's need for a medical facility transformed the sanitarium into a hospital, which is carrying out its mission today.

Medical men like Dr. Benjamin Cory came to the valley as early as 1847. The Gold Rush brought more. They laid the foundation and public-spirited citizens such as Myles O'Connor built upon it.

Others have taken over and are still building. The earliest physicians showed they cared for their communities as well as their patients. Their lives are intertwined with the growth of Santa Clara Valley.

The history of medicine inevitably is an accounting of physicians striving for progress. An effort is made here to reveal the various components of their personalities, rather than the cold chronicling of dates and statistics. Theirs is a long overdue story.

CHAPTER ONE

Lure of the Gold

GOLD HAS ALWAYS turned men's minds. Speak of it softly and lazy ears come to attention. And when the wondrous yellow metal lies on the ground for the taking, all yardsticks to sanity take flight.

That was California shortly after January, 1848, when James Marshall's discovery of the glittering nuggets in a tail-race on the American River injected life into a sleepy coastal land.

The practice of medicine didn't really start in California until the gold triggered the greatest migration of humanity in history. Some doctors, like Elbert P. Jones, already were on the scene when Marshall made his find.

The drawling South Carolina doctor was an editor of the *California Star*, Yerba Buena's first newspaper, when his boss Sam Brannan raced through city streets waving a quinine bottle filled with gold dust while announcing to all—"Gold! Gold from the American River!"

The *Star's* opposition newspaper, the *Californian*, was the first to report the gold strike at Sutter's Mill and it was only natural that Dr. Jones deny it all vigorously in his columns. The two papers also were dueling over whether the town's name should be changed from Yerba Buena to San Francisco. Dr. Jones, egged on by the excitable Mormon, Brannan, editorialized against the change. It was not until a few disgruntled readers stuffed little Dr. Jones in a hogshead and rolled him

around the Plaza that he concurred San Francisco, indeed, was a wonderful name.

By late May, 1948, Dr. Jones found himself swept up in the maelstrom of a village going berserk. Only a few months before, the population had blossomed to 459, with males in the majority by 321 to 138. There were two other doctors in town, John Townsend and Victor J. Fourgeaud. The life of Dr. Townsend was soon to end tragically in the Santa Clara Valley. Dr. Fourgeaud, a learned Southerner, was already playing a significant role in the mad rush for gold. It was he who, at Brannan's insistence, wrote a pamphlet extolling the virtues of a magical new land called California. Its distribution up and down the Mississippi and Ohio River valleys soon had the word, California, on everyone's tongue.

The *Star* and *Californian* were forced to cease publication when printers abandoned their type, grabbed picks and shovels and headed for the "diggings." By June, San Francisco's population had withered to seven persons and it was the same story in other West Coast communities. Drs. Jones, Townsend and Fourgeaud could do nothing else but join the surge into the hills.

The medical men turned miners met with at least moderate success in a few months.

Dr. Jones, half-crazed over his newfound wealth in Sierra streambeds, soon was back

St. Louis in 1849 at the time of Myles P. O'Connor's departure for California. River towns such as St. Louis were flooded with pamphlets describing in exaggerated detail the gold fields awaiting emigrants in the Sierra Nevada.

in San Francisco. It was said he delighted in a daily ritual in which he would sprinkle gold dust on a bedsheet spread on the floor of his room. Casting off his shoes, he would prance around in the powder, squeezing it between his toes. He would then shower himself with the yellow particles while cackling gleefully. Hardly anyone noticed when one day Dr. Jones packed up his precious possessions and went home to Charleston. He died in 1851, leaving a fortune of $200,000.

These were the tales that tantalized the world as news of "Gold in California" was plastered on pub walls in London, clapboard shanties in Chile and riverboat bulletin boards on the Mississippi.

In St. Louis, newspapers were heavy with advertisements asking "all those interested in the California expedition meet at candlelight in the courthouse." A young lawyer, Myles Poore O'Connor, stood on the fringe and listened. An irresistible sense of adventure that ran to the marrow tugged at O'Connor as talk of gold and California dominated every conversation. America's westward marching frontier had bypassed St. Louis. Mired in the humdrum existence of a struggling young attorney in a community well stocked with men of law, O'Connor was ripe for the blandishments about this new paradise on the Pacific.

O'Connor never had lived in any one place too long, which may have contributed to his restlessness. He was born in Abbeyleix, County Leix, Ireland, on May 8, 1823. His family emigrated from this tiny hamlet located fifty miles west of Dublin to England when he was only two years old. For the next thirteen years the family resided in several industrial communities, including Manchester and Bolton.

In 1838, when Myles was 14, his family moved to America. Arriving in New York, the O'Connors found their new home in a chaotic financial state as the country struggled to recover from the crushing Panic of 1837. It took almost three years for the emigrant family to arrange passage to St. Louis, where Myles' uncle, Jeremiah O'Connor, was well established. Jeremiah's prominence in St. Louis affairs (he gave the city a large grant of land and donated the property for the original site of St. Louis University) no doubt made an indelible impression on his young nephew.

Myles was a quiet, studious lad who gained employment when 19 years old in the office of Major U. Wright, an eminent jurist of the day. Myles had three brothers, Matthew, Jerome and James. It was Matthew who recognized Myles' vocation to law. He decided to help finance Myles through St. Louis University, a Jesuit institution. Theirs was a special comradeship. Matthew took part in the War

with Mexico and fought in the Battle of Buena Vista. He died from the effects of wounds in November, 1849, at Sacramento. Myles never forgot Matthew's assistance during those law school days. His feelings were evidenced years later when he memorialized Matthew's name on a hospital chapel in California's Santa Clara Valley.

While in law school, Myles also pressed his studies to become a citizen and he was naturalized in St. Louis Criminal Court on July 27, 1844. Two years later, he was graduated with honors from the university and he immediately began practice of his profession.

The relatively genteel city of St. Louis was especially susceptible to the tales of California's Golden Yellow Fever sweeping the nation late in 1848. Pamphlets and guidebooks such as the one written by Dr. Fourgeaud flooded the emigrant supply towns. Talk of nuggets the sizes of miners' fists was everywhere. The gold, men whispered, dotted the landscape like fallen fruit. Many of the publications—such as Lansford Hastings' popular "Emigrants' Guide" and John C. Fremont's report of his 1842 explorations—exaggerated the true conditions. It was Hastings' publication which informed the star-crossed Donner Party of a "shortcut" around the south end of the Great Salt Lake, a perilous path blamed for delaying the caravan enough to result in the most tragic chapter of all westward travels. News of the Donners' fate that winter of 1846-1847 was shocking, but it was shunted aside and by the spring of 1849 the gold obsession was even more evident.

O'Connor, then 25 years old, digested the pamphlets on the new land. He attended the meetings as companies were formed to rush for gold. Yet O'Connor's interest in pursuing the storied metal was secondary. His plan was to practice law on the booming, building frontier. Success in his chosen profession was his goal and these were the thoughts that occupied his mind as he packed his belongings and went to St. Joseph, Missouri, in early April, 1849.

The fastest route was by water, down the Mississippi to New Orleans, by ship to the Isthmus of Panama or around Cape Horn, and then finally the northward leg to San Francisco. As early as January 17, ships were en route from New York. Most of these gold hunters disembarked at Panama and struggled through hot, malaria-infested jungles to a port on the Pacific Ocean. The backlog there of would-be miners mounted daily because of a shortage of ships. Men bid up to a thousand dollars for a single seat. Meanwhile, the cemetery was filling with American graves. But the wave of humanity kept coming, driven by assurances that California could be reached in only six weeks.

O'Connor at first considered the sea route, but rejected it as too expensive. Although thousands braved blazing temperatures and Gila monsters to make the trek through the American Southwest or Mexico, the Overland Trail from the Missouri River was the most popular. A man needed only to hitch up the family wagon, toss in some food and clothing and head for the setting sun.

St. Joseph was one of several key jumping off points that included Independence and Westport, Missouri, and Kanesville, Iowa. Fanciful gadgets called "goldometers" were offered credulous travelers as indispensable aids for striking it rich. Ministers entreated the travelers not to leave their morals on the east side of the Missouri. Outrageous prices were charged for goods and living space for the waiting thousands was all but impossible to find. Editors added fuel to the gold rush story with far-fetched reports. One humorist spoke of a miner sitting on an 839-pound nugget for sixty-seven days for fear it would be stolen and then offering $27,000 for a plate of pork and beans. The gold seekers were in a gullible mood.

These Argonauts were not to be deterred. They were forewarned of the hardships. As one scout put it:

"Yaas, and every day—rain, hail, cholera, breakdowns, lame mules, sick cows, washouts, prairie fires, flooded coulees, lost horses, dust storms, alkali water. Seventeen miles every day—or you land in the snow and eat each other like the Donner Party done in '46."

Some 20,000 persons were poised on the wide Missouri that morning of April 16 when O'Connor's reins girded his mule team into action. The winter snows were evaporating and prairie grass was sprouting ahead, a necessity to feed the horses and cattle accompanying the wagon trains. In 1849 alone, it was estimated that upwards of 40,000 persons left Missouri river points for California and Oregon. The travelers were mostly young, with men outnumbering women, sixteen to one, and women outnumbering children, three to one. Accompanying the 10,000 wagons were some 36,000 oxen, 18,000 horses, 7,000 mules and cows and 2,000 sheep.

A captain for each wagon train was selected and he made job assignments for members of the company. O'Connor was designated a cook. The trains consisted of forty to fifty wagons and they followed a trail forged years before by such great mountain men as James Bridger, Kit Carson and Thomas Fitzpatrick. In 1843, a young Missouri lawyer had formed the largest wagon train up to that date—100 wagons, 260 men, 130 women, 610 children, and 5,000 cattle. His name was Peter Burnett, who led his train to Oregon and later journeyed south to become California's first governor.

The trail from St. Joe serpentined through northeastern Kansas, then angled north toward the Platte River. O'Connor must have wondered what fate awaited this motley collection of men who sloshed through an exceptionally wet and muddy Midwestern spring. Men pushing handcarts and wheel-barrows, men riding horseback with their life's possessions in their saddlebags, men driving ponderous oxen and fractious mules in wagons ranging in stature from simple flatbeds to sumptuous "prairie schooners." Mustachioed Spaniards and plucky Frenchmen mixed with Kentucky backwoodsmen and Connecticut ministers.

Selection of a mule team left O'Connor in the minority. Most wagons were pulled by oxen which out-numbered the mules, three to one. Horses could not stand the beating the animals had to take day after day. Southerners preferred mules, New Englanders and Midwesterners the oxen. The oxen were slower, averaging only two miles an hour, but the mules were characteristically stubborn, would quit on a tough pull and hated the mud.

Chimney Rock, the giant monolith on the Platte River, was a famous landmark on the Overland and Oregon Trails for emigrants bound for the Far West. It stands in what is now western Nebraska.

(Courtesy of Bancroft Library)

Dr. Amos Batchelder, a gold seeker from Pelham, New Hampshire, wrote:

"A mule's natural disposition is not the most amiable and his inclination not to go the way you want him to is proverbial." Myles O'Connor could only nod a firm assent.

At first sight of the Platte River, vanguard riders of this Golden Army happily informed the wagons they had spotted the "Coast of Nebraska." It was along the Platte that some of the grimmest stories of the early West unfolded. Running five feet deep and a mile wide as the spring thunderstorms rolled across the plains, the roily Platte was both friend and foe. Its waters were life-giving to the travelers, but they also devastated wagons during crossings and more than one emigrant was swept away by the churning currents.

As the travelers followed the Platte within sight of Grand Island, an attenuated sandbar stretching fifty miles in length, the dreaded cholera made itself felt. The Asia-spawned disease had been carried by ship to such ports as New Orleans and had moved up the Mississippi Valley into the emigrant supply towns.

Infected water, nurtured by warming temperatures, encouraged spread of the malady. It showed no favorites, striking down infants and adults alike. Makeshift graves, with tombstones carved from wagon planking, lined the route. Wagon train leaders isolated sufferers and often abandoned them rather than risk contamination of the entire party. The disease, marked by diarrhea, dehydration and shock, claimed victims with amazing suddenness. Smiling and strong in the morning, they often were dead by nightfall.

Between St. Joseph and Fort Laramie, Wyoming, one historian estimated 5,000 graves lined the trail by the end of 1849. A train would no sooner bury a victim and pass around the bend than coyotes and prairie dogs were pawing at the freshly turned earth.

In his latter years, O'Connor would regale friends with stories of the hardships encountered in the 2,000-mile trek. A niece, Mrs. Annette Butler Cremin of Marysville, California, remembers especially his tales of skirmishes with Indians, the buffalo hunts along the Platte and the cholera. But he would laugh in recounting his tribulations in the camp kitchen.

O'Connor, in fact, must have been quite adept at his new job. Sowbelly and biscuits (bacon and hot bread baked in a Dutch oven) were the staples of the trains. "Slamjohns" were the ponderous pancakes. Pickles were eaten as a protection against scurvy. As a luxury, women sometimes rolled out dough on leather wagon seats and made delicious pies out of dried fruit. Buffalo jerky was a popular snack. A not-so-popular necessity was pemmican, which was concocted from the jerky pounded into powder and poured into receptacles until half full. It was then covered with melted buffalo tallow and the whole mess was stirred together and stored for future use.

Man's inhumanity to man was evidenced many times among the emigrants. Cholera-stricken families, abandoned along the trail by their train, were ignored by wagon after wagon. Finally, the pathos of the scene would touch a bypasser and aid was offered. The climbs over such rocky knolls as Windlass Hill in western Nebraska taxed every fiber of the travelers' nerves and muscles. The ascent and descent were so steep the wagons had to be maneuvered with ropes attached to windlasses.

Fort Laramie in eastern Wyoming was a regular stopping place of the wagon trains. Located at the junction of Laramie Creek and the Platte River, it opened as a fur trading post. The walls were 15-foot-thick adobe, with well-fortified blockhouses at each corner of the square fort.

(Courtesy of Bancroft Library)

Despite the sweat and toil expended to conquer such obstacles, little was ever done to make it easier for followers. Emigrants didn't want parties in their wake to pass them because of the scarcity of grass ahead.

Some gold seekers burned property rather than leave it for anyone else. Sand was poured into jettisoned sugar and bacon. On occasion only bleached bones of oxen warned newcomers the water at a spring was alkalied. But then again, a kind-hearted soul might improvise a "poison-water" sign to assist followers.

The constant crises brought out the true character of O'Connor's traveling companions and the lessons in human nature stood him in good stead in the years after he reached the new Eldorado.

"Yet, not withstanding all these drawbacks," O'Connor once wrote in his diary on November 25, 1877, "if I had to make the trip over again, having made known to me what I would endure and suffer and what I would enjoy, I would undertake it with alacrity and pleasurable anticipation."

The wagons, with Chimney Rock bidding a mute farewell, left Nebraska and crawled across Wyoming's high plains. Independence Rock was a historic stop. The huge mountain loaf was covered with etched signatures of those who had gone before. It is believed the rock was named by a party that had halted there on Independence Day.

Fort Laramie, with its mounted troops, gave the forty-niners their first glimpse of an organized settlement since the Missouri River. Then came the tortuous climb over South Pass, a 7,550-foot milestone. This was the Continental Divide where the emigrants could look and marvel that the running water at their feet would find its way to the Pacific Ocean. A variety of routes led the trains to Fort Hall in southeastern Idaho, ten miles north of the present city of Pocatello. Fort Hall was

Fort Hall, as seen by approaching wagon trains in 1849. The fort on the Snake River in Idaho then was 15 years old. It served as the last outpost of civilization for travelers swinging south into the treacherous Humboldt River country en route to Sacramento.

(Courtesy of Bancroft Library)

an important juncture on the Overland Trail. It was here that the travelers had to decide whether to continue their rush to California and its gold, or follow the northern trail to Oregon and its lush timber and farm lands.

And it was at this Snake River outfitting point that it became obvious only the strong would complete the journey. The necessity of averaging seventeen miles a day to reach California's formidable Sierra Nevada range before the first snows intensified the pressure on nerves already frayed by the day-to-day hardships. Some wagons broke down and disintegrated under the incessant pounding. A few persons had quit on the Platte and struck out for their old homes, but by the time the party was beyond South Pass and within sight of the red banner and white-

washed walls of Fort Hall, there was no turning back.

While a handful of the travelers was lured to Oregon, the great mass of the Golden Army swung left at the fork along the swift-running Snake and ground south toward the Ruby Mountains, located in what is now northeastern Nevada. At the base of this range, wells bubble out of the earth to form one of the world's weirdest streams. This freak of nature—a river that comes from nowhere and after 364 miles of wandering disappears into the earth—presented the forty-niners with the greatest peril of their long journey.

The Humboldt was named in 1845 by soldier-explorer John Charles Fremont because of his admiration for a German natural scientist, explorer and philosopher, Baron Alexander von Humboldt, who never saw its bitter, tainted waters. But despite sand, lava rock and alkali, grass grew along the Humboldt and sustained the animals of the caravans. O'Connor sported a three-month growth of beard as the Argonauts trundled through the dust. A merciless sun tortured them in their despair. Those few happy moments along the Missouri River were vague memories. The camaradarie among the gold seekers at Fort Laramie and South Pass was no more. The Humboldt put men to their most stringent test.

"This part of the country," penned the New Hampshire doctor, Amos Batchelder, "is more mountainous than we expected to find it. It is very barren and almost inhabitable. There is not a particle of wood except dwarf willow, wild sage and greasewood . . . The sky has been perfectly cloudless for many days, with one exception . . . Everything is as dry as ashes. Our hands are full of cracks, and the more we wash them in the alkaline water, the worse they crack."

No forty-niner would have believed that this desolate land years later would be populated by such bustling little communities as Elko, Winnemucca and Lovelock. Many emigrants became irrational. The cattle often were too jumpy to milk. In some trains, all dogs were shot for fear their barking would start a stampede or signal Indians of their location.

As wheels dipped to their hubcaps in the lava dust, O'Connor and his associates were forced to don masks. The wagons took turns moving up a notch each day toward the front of the column where there was relief from the dust.

The Indians were a constant menace. Mistreated in the early 1840's by trappers and mountain men, they regarded the newcomers with disdain. Members of the Shoshokoe tribe, often called the Diggers, were completely unpredictable. They would meander into camp, asking for food. They would eat anything in one gulp, including a bolt of tobacco. The braves moved in bands apart from the squaws, going off on hunting sorties. The squaws survived in odd ways. They would form huge circles and thrash the sagebrush to chase grasshoppers and crickets into huge pits. The insects then were turned into "delicacies" by cooking them with hot rocks or by grinding them into coarse cakes.

Many an emigrant visited a Digger camp in a friendly gesture and partook of the Indian food. He was a pale-faced "paleface" when he learned later what he had eaten.

The Diggers skulked behind wagon trains, rushing to abandoned camp sites in search of food or trinkets. As time passed the Diggers learned to sneak up on sleeping parties and fire crippling arrows into the oxen and mules. Unable to travel, the animals were left behind and the starving Indians hurried to claim their suffering prizes.

By the time the trains reached the Humboldt Sink, where the river disappeared into the alkalied terrain, the travelers were in a "very seedy and unsound state," chronicled an Englishman, William Kelly. "They more nearly resembled a batch of invalids crawling in search of a hospital, than a band of adventurous travelers charging the Great Sierra Nevada to jump into the golden valley of the Sacramento. But this lodestar kept up the flagging spirits."

Only such an enticing objective as gold sustained many forty-niners along the Humboldt, which they tabbed "The Valley of the Shadow of Death." Each day was as monotonous as the one before. Up at six o'clock, the emigrants drove until the midday heat chased them to the cover of the nearby willows or cottonwoods or the shadow of the wagons themselves. Men washed down their slender rations with coffee, made almost unpalatable by the alkali water. Some animals dropped dead in their tracks while lapping up the milky liquid. Others were fed "nicotine sandwiches," which consisted of plugs of tobacco between pieces of bacon. And still others were fed alkali water flavored with flour to give it substance.

The Sink brought the travelers to the brink of this summer Hades. Ahead was Destruction Valley, the Forty Mile Desert, the one last hurdle before the cool, beckoning waters of the Carson or Truckee Rivers.

The Humboldt behind it, O'Connor's party rolled out at dusk to avoid the heat of the day, with the Carson as the goal. Powdery dust slowed the wagons to a pace of one mile an hour. Presently, the trail hardened again as the blistering morning

sun took its toll. Kelly, the Englishman whose party followed that of O'Connor's, told of men going mad who had to be tied to their wagons. In this sizzling August cauldron, animals keeled over and their groaning further sickened their departing owners. Thousands of dollars worth of property was cast aside in the grim drive to the Carson. Many persons were met carrying water from the Carson or Truckee to rescue families and friends stalled on the desert. Available water sold for $1 a gallon.

Forty-niner Joseph Goldsborough Bruff counted 82 dead oxen, two horses and a mule in one-tenth of a mile during this stretch. "The sight of the dead," wrote John Wood, "is not so fearful as the living dying. God in Heaven! Could human suffering appease thy wrath, the world would soon be forgiven."

The sight of fresh water on the Carson Valley slope sent the loose stock and some of the Argonauts in a wild dash for the river. Men and animals frolicked in the cool, Sierra-fed stream. Finally, it was necessary to rope some horses and other

The Humboldt River at Lassen's Meadow. This is one of the first sketches of the "Valley of the Shadow of Death" and was made by a government survey team seeking a practicable route west for the railroad.

(Courtesy of Bancroft Library)

James Frazier Reed and his wife, Margret, were members of the star-crossed Donner Party. Reed, who fought in the Battle of Santa Clara, was a leader in the attempt to retain the California state capitol in San Jose. His grandson, Frazier O. Reed, was a San Jose Hospital trustee for 30 years.

(Courtesy of Clyde Arbuckle)

animals and drag them away so they would not drink themselves to death. O'Connor's caravan followed the river into the foothills and decided to cross the mighty Sierra via the route blazed by scout Kit Carson and John C. Fremont five years previously.

Despite the 4,000-foot climb up the east face of the mountains that led to 8,573-foot-high Carson Pass, this route was preferred by many emigrant trains. The travelers could not help but glance northward, where three years before the Donner Party had been halted by nature some fifty miles away. Even though it still was late summer, they tried to imagine the snow and storms that hit this region. There was always at least one member of a caravan who knew the Donner tragedy in detail, and it was spiced with new stories at each retelling.

George and Jacob Donner had leagued with twenty-seven other residents of Springfield, Illinois, to lead a party to California. Lansford Hastings' glowing accounts had spurred the Donner brothers and James Frazier Reed to find this new land where "December is as pleasant as May." Reed, born in Ireland of Polish parents, was a man of indomitable spirit tested in the Black Hawk War when he

fought in the same company with a gawky young lawyer named Abraham Lincoln.

All told, the party numbered eighty-seven when it set out in the spring of 1846. Misguided by Hastings' insistence he had found a shortcut to California, the Donner-Reed train ignored the Fort Hall route and struck out from southwest Wyoming through the Wasatch Mountains and then around the south end of the Great Salt Lake. Cursing Hastings with every step, the party struggled through the saline sand. The disastrous trek across the salt flats had cost Reed almost all of his belongings. Reed's mood was understandable several weeks later when he saw a teamster, John Snyder, lashing his oxen unmercifully on a hard pull on the Humboldt near Battle Mountain. Reed intervened, a fight ensued and Reed killed Snyder with a knife. Reed was banished from the emigrant train and he rode on ahead to Sutter's Fort to seek help for his family and other dispairing members of the caravan. Snows impeded his return and he retreated to San José. There he found Americans sympathetic with his plight, but more concerned with the budding War with Mexico. Reed decided to help the Americans in hope they would help him and he actually commanded a company on the right of the

Myles P. O'Connor and thousands of other emigrants crossed this Carson Pass trail in the Sierra Nevada in 1849 in the rush to the California gold fields. The picture of the 8,000-foot pass was taken in early summer.

(Courtesy of the Rev. Robert Duryea)

artillery in the Battle of Santa Clara. At that moment, his family and others of the Donner Party were snowbound and starving in the Sierra. San Joséans responded by petitioning for a relief expedition and in Yerba Buena seven hundred dollars was raised on the spot. A series of relief expeditions that continued into April of 1847 finally brought out the Donner Party shrouded in tales of cannibalism. Reed, despite increasing misfortune that began on the salt flats, miraculously rescued his entire family alive, including his wife, Marg-

ret; three children, Patty, 8, Jimmy, 5, and Tommy, 3, and a stepdaughter, Virginia, 12. Of the original party of eighty-seven, forty perished.

(Reed and many of the other Donner Party survivors settled in Santa Clara Valley. He bought a large tract of land close to the pueblo of San José. During the gold rush, he added to his wealth and in 1850 became one of California's first subdividers. He is said to have spent twenty thousand dollars to help promote San José as California's state capital. He died in 1874. Sev-

20

eral city streets, including Reed, Margaret (this spelling was a later alteration of Margret), Virginia and Keyes, bear names of the family members. Jacob Donner's daughter, Mary, was adopted by the Reeds. She married a lawyer and former San José mayor, Sherman O. Houghton, in 1859, but tragedy continued to stalk her and she died a year later during childbirth. Frances, daughter of George Donner, lived with the Reeds for awhile. Her sister, Eliza, came to San José later from Sacramento—and in a strange twist of fate — became Houghton's second wife. Reed's grandson, Frazier O. Reed, was a prominent realtor as well as a San José Hospital trustee for thirty years.)

O'Connor, confronted with rugged climbs up steep cliffs, found California no less difficult a challenge than Nebraska or Nevada. Wagons often had to be dismantled and dragged up precipices by windlasses. Finally, on August 17, 1849, O'Connor looked out over the sugar pines and firs to the broad San Joaquin Valley. California, at last!

The Golden Yellow Fever billowed inside the glassy-eyed forty-niners as they wound down through the Sierra foothills.

These ragged and weary men had "seen the elephant," a common expression meaning they had experienced a harrowing ordeal and although they had no regrets over their decision to face the hardships of westward travel, they certainly wanted no part in repeating the performance.

The journey from Missouri had taken 122 days, accomplished by averaging a little more than fifteen miles a day. O'Connor's train had made good time, although others had not fared so well. Historians estimated that only about half of forty-niner wagons leaving the Midwest jumping off points ever reached the Carson River and only one-third made the straw-brown valleys of California.

The graves of men, women and children and the stench of fallen oxen were grim vestiges of the long trek. The survivors had to be a hardy lot. Historian Valeska Bari congratulated California at receiving the cream of American manhood: "The strongest pushed on to their goal, the weaklings died on the trail and the cowards never left home."

MRS. MYLES O'CONNOR

CHAPTER TWO

Building of a Fortune

DISILLUSIONMENT greeted Myles O'Connor soon after he had bade goodbye to his faithful mules and checked in at General Augustus Sutter's Fort in Sacramento.

He was eager to begin a law practice and grow with the country. But where? The new state of California had seen its population shoot from 14,000 in 1848 to 100,000 by the time the 26-year-old O'Connor arrived. It was a mobile, fluid force streaming up and down the mountain country in pursuit of the precious metal.

Mining camps leapfrogged through the wilderness, often enjoying short lives when a vein played out or news of another strike lured the prospectors elsewhere. The practice of law necessitated a semblance of civilization in an orderly society. O'Connor found little of this in the mad, frenzied world of the forty-niners.

It was understandable that gold—a word mentioned 409 times in the Bible—transformed clergymen as well as doctors, college professors, farmers and merchants into amateur miners.

San Francisco, San José, Sonoma and Monterey became virtual "ghost towns" as residents swept into the gold country. Harry Bee, the San José city jailer, did not enjoy being left home alone. Holding the keys on 10 prisoners, including two charged with murder, Bee tried in vain to find someone to take his place. Failing at that, he outfitted his prisoners with picks and shovels, pointed toward the hills and had a good thing going until nervous miners objected.

O'Connor stacked away his law books and became a miner out of necessity. There was little call for a man of his profession and he was running low on funds. He then met his second disappointment. Possession of mining tools and boundless energy did not guarantee a man immediate wealth. Gold hunters had been combing the hills for a full eighteen months before O'Connor's arrival. Most of the good locations had been appropriated. Abandoned diggings and marginal properties were all that was left in many regions. O'Connor moved aimlessly through the gold country.

James W. Marshall, the New Jersey carpenter who had stumbled across gold at Sutter's Mill, found more of the metal at Deer Creek, 60 miles northeast of Sacramento in the summer of 1848. A surly, heavy-drinking eccentric who imagined he could communicate with spirits, he moved on to other diggings. (It was ironic that Marshall, who started the greatest gold rush in history, died in abject poverty in 1885, feeling he never was properly rewarded for his discovery.) Marshall's find lured other miners to the Deer Creek-Grass Valley region.

An incident of a wandering cow focused attention on Grass Valley and changed O'Connor's life.

George Knight, as the story goes, lost a cow in Boston Ravine near the town.

Sutter's Fort in Sacramento, completed in 1843, was a goal of travelers such as Myles O'Connor in their long trek to California. The fort provided food and shelter for pioneers upon their arrival. It was a monument to General John Augustus Sutter, whose dreams of building an empire were smashed by the coming of the gold seekers.

(Courtesy of Bancroft Library)

Knight was chasing the animal when he stubbed his toe on an outcropping of white rock. He peered down to discover the rock veined with yellow streaks. It was gold quartz. Although quartz mining had been tried in scattered areas before, Knight's unwitting find pointed up that gold indeed did run deep into the rocks and perhaps the mysterious source of the metal—the Mother Lode—had been found. Although no one knows what happened to the sore-toed Knight, the site of his find became the famed Gold Hill Mine, which produced four million dollars in ore in its first four years. This discovery on June 6, 1850, caught O'Connor's attention and he decided to make Grass Valley his permanent home.

Unlike O'Connor, most gold seekers had no plans to remain in California indefinitely. They wanted to make their "pile" and return to their old homes to live in luxury the rest of their lives. While O'Connor was engaged in mining, the word became known that he had a legal background. As the area grew, he found he was being called upon more and more for legal advice. Dusting off his law books, it wasn't long before he was practicing his chosen profession, at least part time.

O'Connor was not an exception among the early miners, who represented a wide range in cultural, social and intellectual backgrounds. Writer Bayard Taylor, after a visit to the gold fields, commented:

"Among the number of miners scattered through the different gulches, I met daily with men of education and intelligence, from all parts of the United States. It was never safe to presume on a person's character from his dress or appearance. A rough, dirty, sunburned fellow with unshorn beard, quarring at the bottom of some rocky hole, might be a graduate of one of the finest colleges in the country. I found plenty of men who were not outwardly distinguishable from the inveterate trapper or mountaineer, but who, a year before, had been physicians, lawyers or editors. It was this infusion of intelligence which gave the gold-hunting communities, notwithstanding their barbaric experior and mode of life, an order and individual security which at first sight seemed little less than marvelous."

Some miners boasted of their "Midas touch" as every rock they uncovered seemed to hide a placer of gold. A young "greenhorn" named Davenport asked some miners where he might make a strike. They exchanged winks and pointed up a bleak canyon, an apparent wild goose chase. But the boy fooled them and found his bonanza. On the first day he panned 77 ounces of pure gold, and on the second, 90. After two days he showed the miners 167 ounces, worth $2,700, triggering a wild rush up the supposedly barren ravine.

One nugget, called "The Monumental," was the biggest taken out of the earth. It weighed 148 pounds and 8 ounces and measured 15 inches long, six inches wide and four inches thick. Uncovered in Calaveras County, it was sold in San Francisco for $40,000. Ever-present gold strikes,

or rumors of them, kept the mining camps buzzing. Although the Argonauts took out an average of one ounce ($20) a day, most were less fortunate. The work was backbreaking. Standing in icy water 12 hours a day or swinging picks at granite creek banks took its toll on the miners' health. At dusk, they returned to cheerless shacks or tents and tried to muster enough strength to cook. A staple was bread leavened with saleratus and baked on a hot stone or fried in a pan. The bread, poorly cooked beans and greasy pork was washed down with coffee ground from green beans. A varied diet was difficult, especially with potatoes selling at one dollar a pound and apples and eggs at fifty cents apiece.

Dr. Benjamin Cory, the first San José physician, detailed the rough living conditions at Gold Placero camp in a letter to his family in 1848. He complained of the one dollar charge to wash a single handkerchief, compared to 12½ cents in his native Ohio. "I live somewhat roughly in the mountains. I have slept on the ground in the open air the last five months. I frequently cook my meat on a stick, or in the ashes. I have lived on dried beans and coffee without sugar or cream . . . and I use a stone for a pillow . . . But this is the richest gold country on the face of the globe. Gold almost looks like a worthless toy—I have seen so much."

A combination of the blazing sun, damp mining conditions and an inadequate diet sickened many prospectors. Diarrhea, dysentery, scurvy and severe cases of poison oak were common. The patients had to cure themselves and the self-prescribed and administered overdoses of calomel, quinine and laudanum sometimes were worse than the disease.

At first, prospectors gathered gold by

washing gravel in a pan beside a stream. The gold settled to the bottom and was painstakingly collected. In many high tributaries of the Sacramento and San Joaquin Rivers, there were only 85 working days a year. When high water or inclement weather chased the miners from the creekbeds, they turned to the "dry diggings." Dirt was thrown in the air and the gold winnowed by the wind. But this was a tedious process and later such devices as rockers, cradles and long toms were improvised. One refinement introduced to aid in gold washing was mercury. It amalgamated with the gold while excluding other foreign matter. The gold then could be isolated again by vaporizing the mercury in a retort. The first mercury mine on the North American continent had been discovered in 1845 at New Almaden near San José and the mercury was of great value to gold hunters.

With these devices, many men could work together and share their findings. Boxes and troughs were constructed and the gravel was shoveled onto a screen. Water carried the fine sand and gold over the edge of the box into another container. An elaborate system of flumes, or V-shaped wooden aqueducts, was developed. The water often had to be brought into the gold claim from a distance of many miles. By the early 1850's, the solitary miner—with his rusty pick, battered pan and floppy eared burro—began to disappear. Men working alone, humming the plaintive strains of such ditties as "Mary Blaine," "Oh, Susanna," and "Dearest Mae," were on the wane.

Grass Valley had grown from a couple of cabins to an active town of gold-oriented citizens by mid-1851. Four miles away, Nevada City also was taking shape. When gold was discovered there in 1849, an en-

terprising physician named A. B. Caldwell promptly freighted in a load of supplies. The camp was known as Caldwell's Upper Store since the good doctor earlier had opened a store further down Deer Creek. Dr. Caldwell's store was Nevada City's first house and the physician later moved to San José where he and his son were greatly respected for their medical work.

O'Connor, fascinated by the challenge of extracting the gold from the quartz in a fashion economically feasible, kept an eye on the Grass Valley hills for signs of a rich lode. Then, on August 2, 1852, O'Connor and four others—H. and T. Doyle, L. Rudolph and H. Fuller—filed a big claim.

O'Connor evidently found a potential money-maker in quartz, but he and other miners were all but ruined by the expensive methods for recovering the ore. When surface samples hinted a gold vein might be found below, tunnels were driven into the quartz. It was then blasted out, brought to the surface and crushed in large "stamp mills" until the gold could be extracted. A Dr. Rodgers promoted a "smelter" and sold shares to the miners. His idea was to heat the quartz in a furnace to a high temperature and maintain it for forty-eight hours. It might sound like a hairbrained scheme today, but the mining community was desperate in those days. People came from afar to watch the experiment as Dr. Rodgers went into action. He heated the rock, waited and began the cooling process. He then raked out what he believed would be gold nuggets. Instead he found rocks, a little charred and warm, but still rocks.

By 1860, gold rushes were beginning in Nevada's Comstock Lode, the Fraser River in British Columbia, Canada, and the Pikes Peak region in Colorado. O'Connor de-

A contemporary drawing by Charles Nahl of a trail in the California gold fields. Indians, Chinese, Hawaiians, Mexicans and Americans were among the many nationalities combing the Sierra Nevada for the precious metal.

clined to join the stampede of miners to the new areas. Grass Valley, with its as yet unspectacular but more stable quartz mining operations, began taking on an aura of permanence while neighboring camps disintegrated into ghost towns.

O'Connor filed claim after claim in quest of a big stake. Copper and other minerals came within his sphere of interest. Slowly, as his mining developments began to yield profits, he was able to spend more time in his law office. Grass Valley was broadening its base each year and the big business mining operations required constant legal counsel.

Grass Valley was an exciting town in the Fifties. Lola Montez, the captivating bru-nette for whom King Ludvig of Bavaria had surrendered his throne, moved into a home on Mill Street with a pet bear on a leash. Her appearance upset the female population no end.

In 1854, O'Connor developed a romantic interest of his own. His quickening of the pulse in meeting Mrs. Amanda Butler Young was understandable. A woman in the gold country, especially one so pretty, gracious and independent, merited attention. Mrs. Young was a widow who had moved to Grass Valley to be near her brother, John Butler. Her husband and two-year-old son had been killed by lightning in Ohio. Mrs. Young had eloped at the age of 16, alienating her parents. Only her brother stood by her and she gladly joined him in California after the tragic loss of her own family.

In those early mining days, the country was populated almost entirely by men. Any woman who happened along could do no wrong. In one camp near Grass Valley, a shopkeeper charged one dollar admission just for a glimpse of a bonnet and a pair of ladies' shoes. In another ravine, a miner found a bonnet along the trail. His colleagues tacked it on a big post and held an impromptu dance around it all night. The men out-numbered women, ten to one, and

it was impossible in many places to convict a woman of any crime. In Shasta City, a miner was hard-pressed to finance his wedding until he hit upon the idea of charging admission to the ceremony. The miners were so interested in seeing the new bride they paid five dollars a head to witness the marriage, and the bridegroom collected a sum large enough to start housekeeping in a grand style.

Myles O'Connor was a small man. But even at 5 ft. 8 in. he towered over the tiny Mrs. Young. His gray eyes would twinkle as he escorted her down Grass

Grass Valley, California, a lithograph of the early 1850's. Chinese in foreground carry loads on ends of poles. Quartz mining in the region attracted the former St. Louis lawyer, Myles P. O'Connor, and he built his fortune there between 1849 and 1884.

(Courtesy of Huntington Library)

Valley's dusty, winding streets. They were married on December 7, 1862, in a remarkable union that lasted 47 years. It was fitting that the ceremony was performed by the Rev. Thomas Dalton, the Catholic pastor for the Grass Valley area.

Father Dalton had come to the community in 1855, a graduate of the well-known All Hallows College in Dublin, Ireland. His vibrant personality, massive frame and white-thatched leonine head made him a standout figure and he had innumerable friends among Protestants and Catholics alike. Father Dalton and O'Connor, both born in Ireland, found they had a lot in common and they worked closely together to foster the church's growth in their area.

Father Dalton's fetching way was illustrated in a story told by Mrs. William Leet of San José. Mrs. Leet was the daughter of Edward McLaughlin of Grass Valley, a prominent merchant who later was to become a treasured right arm of O'Connor's in the Santa Clara Valley. The McLaughlins were pioneers who had come to Nevada County from Kentucky. They were serious, deeply religious persons who were not Catholics at the time. Mrs. Leet, relating the story passed down by her mother, said: "The sight of good Father Dalton peacefully riding along with his missionary kit on the back of a mule, absorbed in contemplation, was to be an inspiration. Somehow or other, I was inexpressibly drawn to the man, and whenever he preached in the church, I was sure to go and listen to him. When my first child was born, I determined that I should have none other baptize my baby than Father Dalton."

In his later years, Father Dalton had many assistants. The story was often told of how he would test the virtue of a new assistant, and sometimes pull a little rank on him as well. On a cold January day in 1868, a call came in for a priest to visit a dying man in the hills five miles away. Normally, the two priests took turns on such visits. This time, it was Father Dalton's turn. His new aide, Father Lawrence Kennedy, entered the parlor after saying the last Mass to find his superior warming his stocking feet by the fire. Father Dalton said:

"Father Kennedy, I understand there's a man in a bad way over by the Yuba."

"There is," said Kennedy.

"It's snowing hard," said Dalton.

"It is," said Kennedy.

"It's a good five miles," said Dalton.

"It's all of that," said Kennedy.

"It's freezing cold and a stiff wind's blowing," said Dalton.

"Yes, that's true," said Kennedy.

"I wonder if the sick call can wait," said Dalton.

"It can't," said Kennedy.

"Well," said Dalton, "you'd better go, Father. You've got your shoes on."

And Father Kennedy, with chin up and eyes straight ahead, went out and made the call.

Mrs. Cremin, a niece of O'Connor's, many years later remembered an incident in which Father Dalton stopped by O'Connor's office. The priest was seeking funds for a new fence around the cemetery.

"Would you donate $100 for the new fence?" O'Connor was asked.

O'Connor immediately granted the request and then remarked wistfully:

"If you had not been so specific, Father, the offering would have been ten times as much."

The comradeship between the two grew over the length of their association, span-

The varied means of mining in California are shown in sketch of the 1850s. Left to right: operating rocker, washing with a pan, pushing loaded car out of tunnel, lifting bucket to head of shaft, digging tunnels, using long tom, shoveling "dirt" into line of sluices, and the flume.

(Courtesy of Huntington Library)

ning 19 years. O'Connor was instrumental in bringing five Sisters of Mercy to Grass Valley on August 20, 1863, to teach school and to operate an orphanage.

Although O'Connor had been earning a reasonable wage from his mining interests and law practice for many years, the beginning of his fortune came on May 8, 1863. O'Connor and two partners, Edward and John Coleman, discovered gold-laden quartz a mile and a half east of Grass Valley. This became the famed Idaho Mine, later called the Idaho-Maryland. The mine developed slowly, with only a low grade quartz showing for two years. In 1865, its operations were re-organized. Still, the returns were small and in May, 1866,

the mine was closed down for 16 months. Then, in September, 1867, the Idaho was incorporated and full-scale tunneling of the mountain began. It proved a veritable bonanza. The adjacent Eureka Mine had become the most valuable on the West Coast, producing $2,000 in gold a day. The Idaho was as rich an operation, but on a smaller scale. From 1868 to 1877, the Idaho's receipts came to $4,589,255.

Other mines, such as the Empire, North Star, Gold Hill and Golden Center, had dotted the canyon walls as Grass Valley became the most famous quartz mining town in the Far West. The Empire and North Star, over a century of operation, produced $80 million in gold. The Empire

30

has had no rival in the United States, with the exception of the Homestake Mine at Lead, South Dakota. After the Empire's founding in 1850 by George Roberts, its ownership passed on to an Englishman, James Pierce. He sold the mine for $150,-000 in 1872 after he thought it had been "worked out." The new owners re-financed the mine, putting down tunnels totaling 190 miles in length, and the profits were great. Pierce purchased 88 acres in the mission town of Santa Clara immediately west of the present Carmelite Monastery, the property eventually becoming the site of William Wilson Junior High School. Pierce also founded the Pacific Manufacturing Company in Santa Clara, exemplifying the wealth that poured into the Santa Clara Valley one way or another from the Grass Valley mines.

O'Connor had come to California to practice law, but found gold. Yet so many thousands came for the gold and found little or none, staying on as farmers and businessmen or returning home if they could afford the passage. Some men made fortunes out of the mines, including automobile builder John M. Studebaker, meat packer Phillip Danforth Armour and George Hearst, father of newspaper publisher William Randolph Hearst.

A quiet charm and inherent honesty made O'Connor a popular figure around Grass Valley, which had grown to five thousand on the strength of solid mining and dairying interests. In 1859, O'Connor decided at the age of 36 to embark on a third career—politics. The obstacles were great. He was a strong Democrat in a strong Republican County. And he en-dorsed the ideas of Stephen Douglas, the volatile little presidential opponent of the gangling attorney from Illinois, Abraham Lincoln. But O'Connor won easily and served in the California State Assembly for the 1859-60 term. He introduced a bill, which became law, establishing in 1860 the boundaries of the City and County of San Francisco.

O'Connor's arrival in Sacramento launched a career of 17 years as a public servant. In 1860, he was elected Justice of the Peace for Grass Valley and voters returned him to the post nine straight times. State office beckoned again, and in 1869, O'Connor sought a seat in the Senate. Again he bucked big odds in a Republican area and won. As a senator, he earned respect up and down the state. In the 21st session of the body (1874-75), O'Connor reached the zenith of his political career. Besides looking after his own constituents, he introduced 11 bills and served on 13 committees. When party officials considered inauguration ceremonies for the new governor, they asked O'Connor to manage the festivities.

Despite a retiring personality, O'Connor proved an effective legislator. His quiet, behind-the-scene operations merited little publicity, probably accounting for the fact his many deeds in public service often were overlooked by contemporary historians.

There is no question, however, that Myles O'Connor's forceful bearing in his law court and state office contributed greatly to bridging the chasm between the roaring days of the forty-niner and the era of California's domestication.

CHAPTER THREE

Life on Two Continents

A ROLLING ATLANTIC OCEAN buffeted the ship that cool May morning in 1874 as Myles and Amanda O'Connor watched the New York City skyline disappear under wisps of fog in the distance.

The destination was Europe, long a goal of O'Connor who wanted to retrace the steps of his boyhood. Mrs. O'Connor had visions of Parisian shops and Roman art galleries. Grass Valley was a dim memory now. O'Connor's mining interests for many years had been paying him generously, up to fifteen thousand dollars a month at times. He was near the end of his legislative career and for five years he and Mrs. O'Connor had traveled to various corners of America. Grass Valley hadn't let their departure go unnoticed, nor had Sacramento. Workers at the Eureka Mine, showing the friendship felt for the O'Connors by townspeople, presented them with a valuable piece of transparent quartz crystal. Governor Newton Booth pressed into O'Connor's hand a carefully drafted letter of introduction to important personages in Europe, sparking a smile on the senator's face as he imagined himself as a California ambassador without portfolio.

The O'Connors, pale and nervous, were barely out of sight of Long Island when they quickly left the ship's rail and returned to their cabins. Seasickness made the early days of the voyage a wretched experience.

The O'Connors' first visit abroad spanned a full year and was one of their most extensive. The itinerary covered countries from Great Britain to Russia. In Ireland, O'Connor eagerly sought out the scene of his birth. Leaving his wife in Dublin, he journeyed the fifty miles to Abbeyleix on June 11 with great anticipation. Although he was not quite certain what to expect, the visit proved very disappointing.

"I saw not a soul who knew me or our family—save one man, a Carroll—who knew my father and showed me the house in which I was born," O'Connor penned in his diary.

If a theme guided the O'Connor travels, it was an unremitting pursuit of art. Their diaries were filled with critiques and comments on the art treasures in Europe's galleries and cathedrals.

Sharp criticism of the paintings of the "Old Masters" by the rascally American writer, Mark Twain, during his ventures abroad provoked the California couple.

"I am disgusted with Mark Twain's deriding of the Old Masters," wrote O'Connor. "I wouldn't trade one work of an Old Master for all the moderns we have seen so far."

After visits to Paris and Antwerp, Mrs. O'Connor seconded her husband's thoughts. Twain is nothing more than "a sacrilegeous slanderer," she wrote.

World traveling had its ups and downs, the O'Connors discovered, and she was particularly depressed one rainy June day in Ireland when her husband had gone to consult a Dr. Kidd. Apparently upset herself, she noted:

"If only I could feel well; I would be contented in any position in life. I sometimes get very, very—oh, so weary of life. I do nothing and am nothing. I sometimes feel the world would be higher if I were not in it."

The O'Connors were continuously touched by the plight of Europe's working people and the sordid state of their hand-to-mouth existences. Amanda commented one day after viewing the sumptuous estate of an Irish lord in Killarney: "While that lord is entertaining his gay friends as they chase deer around the grounds, millions of poor wretches are idle and half-starved."

Women around the world, especially in the United States, were pressing for a higher place in society in the 1870's. O'Connor's sense of humor burst through during their stop in Prague in late summer. He wrote:

"One feature seen here . . . exemplifies the results of women's efforts for equality of rights. We saw women digging, picking, shoveling and wheeling dirt from a high embankment being removed for construction of some large edifice. I would like to have seen here our American advocates of equality, that they might rejoice with their sisters; for here in this far-off land, perfect equality of the sexes is a fixed fact, and this priceless situation has been accomplished peaceably, without bloodshed or the ballot."

O'Connor's jocular remarks were footnoted three days later in Moscow when he penned: "Nor do the masses of Russia, with all their wantings of education and civilization, think it is disgraceful to have

the weaker sex engage in this kind of hard labor."

The 1874-1875 sojourn was no doubt the happiest of fourteen visits to Europe for the couple, who spent most of their next thirty years traveling. They sipped Bohemian beer in Prague ("to refresh the inner man—we are becoming civilized"), climbed the 292 steps in the leaning eight-story Tower of Pisa, sampled new varieties of Italian wines and took moonlight rides to the Roman Colosseum.

Rome, the heart of Christendom, won them over immediately. Following a ride to the Villa Borghese, O'Connor gasped:

"The whole panorama of the Eternal City is before us. How wonderful to gaze for the first time upon the mighty spot which has filled the world for twenty-two centuries with its life and deeds."

The couple toured southern Europe in the spring of 1875 and then returned to Grass Valley. They turned over their residence to the Sisters of Mercy, who had come to the community to help Father Dalton in 1863. Bidding goodbye again to their friends, the O'Connors led vagabond lives for the next few years. In 1877, they once more were off to Europe. They spent the second of ten winters in Rome, idly enjoying the life of the city. They were among the millions who mourned at the Vatican on February 7, 1878, upon the death of Pope Pius IX.

In quiet moments, the couple discussed a new home in California. The name of San José often entered their conversations. Its equable climate, in contrast to the rigorous temperatures of Grass Valley, was especially attractive. Mrs. O'Connor had visited San José in 1876 while her husband was wrapping up his political career. She had been a guest of Mrs. Anne Murphy, whose husband Bernard was twice a state senator and three times a mayor of San José.

"Three weeks in San José," Mrs. O'Connor recalled. "Mrs. Murphy assisted in making my visit pleasant indeed. San José is a delightful place with charming drives in every direction. I trust one day to have a home there. I am sure Mr. O'Connor will like it equally as well as I do."

On November 1, 1879, the O'Connors moved to San José where they were quartered at the fashionable Auzerais House on Santa Clara Street, the city's finest hostelry. It was a wet winter and four months later they left for San Francisco, Los Angeles and finally Baltimore. The Maryland city, cradle of Catholicism in America, became the home base for the ever-restless couple between 1880 and 1884.

It was in Baltimore that a close friendship was established between the O'Connors and Archbishop James Gibbons, who in 1886 became America's second cardinal. Archbishop Gibbons discussed with the O'Connors in many meetings his support of the new labor movement and his opposition to plans for setting up Catholic parishes on the basis of racial or national grouping. Between 1880 and 1920, it was no wonder he was the most influential Catholic clergyman in America. O'Connor also became acquainted with Bishop John J. Keane of Richmond, who was to pioneer in the founding of the Catholic University of America at Washington, D.C. Perhaps as a result of associations such as these, Mrs. O'Connor decided to become a Catholic. Her conversion took place on May 11, 1884, in Baltimore.

That summer, the O'Connors went by train to San José and purchased a home-

Edward McLaughlin, prominent businessman and philanthropist in both Grass Valley and San Jose. He was Myles O'Connor's closest friend and supervised construction of the sanitarium while the O'Connors were abroad. His name is perpetuated by McLaughlin Avenue.

site on the northeast corner of Second and Reed Streets. The stately, three-story residence cost forty thousand dollars to complete. San José charmed the O'Connors, not only because it was considered one of the prettiest cities in California, but because so many of their old Grass Valley friends had moved there. Edward McLaughlin, a San José resident since 1868, had built a home at Seventh and Reed and pointed out the Second Street site for

O'Connor's residence. The O'Connor fortune upon his arrival in San José was estimated at two million dollars.

A long-simmering idea to build a home for the aged and the needy began to take shape and in 1887 O'Connor decided to go ahead with the project. A compassion for orphans and the infirmed prompted his plan, which also added an important new interest to his life. Mrs. O'Connor often had complained in her diary of the debilitating effect of idleness upon her husband. She once noted in Florence: "Mr. O'Connor is miserable in health and restless of mind. If he had something to keep his mind and body engaged, I think he would feel much better and more contented and happy." That "something" in the judge's future became the San José Sanitarium.

O'Connor left details for the institution's construction in the hands of his confidante, Edward McLaughlin, and in the spring of 1888 the couple left for Europe once more. On April 24 they stopped off in San Francisco and turned over to Archbishop Patrick William Riordan a deed of trust for the sanitarium property. The property, as specified by O'Connor, would be used for a "sanitarium for the sick, a home for the aged, an asylum for orphans and a school for children." Archbishop Riordan would arrange for the Daughters of Charity of St. Vincent de Paul, or another religious order if necessary, to take over control of the building, to be called the San José Sanitarium and Home.

While pleasure and the arts dominated the O'Connors' early travels, an overpowering pursuit of health became driving factors in later years. Famed spas in Germany and Czechoslovakia lured them again and again. The O'Connors "took

the waters" at Carlsbad and Marienbad. It involved frequent dips in hot alkaline-sulphur baths. O'Connor sought relief for liver and digestive complaints while his wife fretted over rheumatism and the gout. Mrs. O'Connor's temper flared at Carlsbad in May, 1890. She wrote San José friends:

"Mr. O'Connor has been taking the water and finds it is beginning to stir up his liver . . . We have the same doctor and he's quite as parrot-like as ever—the same old lingo about 'our water' and his list of rich people. The doctors here are detestable. Mr. O'Connor went to the doctor and asked his fee. He said, 'Twenty-five florins for the first consultation and ten for each visit.' Mr. O'Connor told him, 'I won't pay it.' The doctors here are the one great drawback to a person's perfect bliss."

By 1895, a new "water cure" was under experimentation by Father Sebastian Kneipp, a priest in Worishofen, Germany. The O'Connors hailed the new hydrotherapy and partook of the treatments regularly. The "cure" became known as "Kneippism" and consisted of ice water baths, vigorous activity in the sunshine and occasional walks bare-footed in the snow.

"Today it is snowing," Mrs. O'Connor penned to sisters in San José. "This morning it rained and hailed, then turned to snow. Yet many people are out in their bare feet. To think such treatment can be good for sciatica, rheumatism and even lung diseases. It really is wonderful."

There were constant stories—of a clergyman with consumption trying the water cure as a last resort and recovering, or of a ten-year-old girl dying of diphtheria. The girl's mother related the experience to the O'Connors. "You can imagine my

35

feelings," she said, "seeing my darling with a burning fever and a dreadful sore throat, plunged into ice cold water and then sponged off every half hour or oftener."

"But," Mrs. O'Connor added, "the child recovered and there is no doubt she would have died with any other treatment. We will have to have a Kneipp treatment center in San José."

Important personages from royalty to the religious frequented Father Kneipp's village. Cardinal Gibbons undertook the treatment in July of 1895 and he and the O'Connors renewed old friendships. Although Kneippism reached great popularity before the turn of the century, the priest died in 1897 and his treatment waned with the advance of medicine.

Various maladies continued to plague the retired San José attorney and judge. Once in Rome, he was indisposed with erysipelas, the infectious skin disease blistering his face around the eyes. His eyesight began to fail in 1895 and treatment for cataracts both in Germany and the United States proved unsuccessful. He underwent an operation on July 10, 1899, but to no avail. Mrs. O'Connor sadly described her husband's appearance during a stop in France three months after the surgery:

"He is well-muffled up when he goes out and also when he is in the house. He has to have two silk handkerchiefs on his head, then his eyes covered with a patch, then a long veil over the eye and around his head . . . If you met him you probably would not know him—with his steamer cap and visor over the eyes. But in the streets of Paris such things are not as observed as in the little village of San José."

By 1901, O'Connor barely could distinguish light from dark. He underwent

examinations by New York specialists and the next year decided to undergo a series of operations at St. Joseph's Hospital in Milwaukee, Wisconsin. But it was no use. The blindness was to plague him the last seven years of his life.

As citizens of two continents, the O'Connors' lives took on new meaning with the advent of their San José project. With each country visited, they sought out pictures, statuary, stained glass windows, linens, religious articles, house furnishings and art treasures for the new sanitarium.

The highlight of their travels took place in December, 1888. Pope Leo XIII was celebrating the golden jubilee of his ordination to the priesthood. Every ruler in Europe, save King Humbert of Italy, was in attendance. President Grover Cleveland, through Cardinal Gibbons, presented the pontiff with a bound copy of the American Constitution, a gift which greatly pleased him. On January 2, 1889, through the intercession of the president of the American College in Rome, Monsignor O'Connell, the O'Connors were permitted to attend the Mass of the Holy Father in his

The Myles P. O'Connor residence, Second and Reed Streets, in the mid-Nineties. It was turned over to the Sisters of Notre Dame for an orphanage. It later was enveloped by Notre Dame High School.

(Courtesy of San Jose Historic Landmarks Commission)

private chapel. Afterward, they were introduced to the pontiff.

"He seemed to have heard of us," Mrs. O'Connor recalled in her diary. "When our name was told him, he said, 'From San Jose?' He asked a few questions, then in giving us his blessings he placed his hands upon Mr. O'Connor's head a second time and said, 'A very special blessing for you.' He placed his hand upon my cheek as he finished his remarks. I asked him to bless the little things I had in my hands. He noticed especially a crucifix and took it tenderly in his hands. I then asked him to bless the hospital and chapel we were building and he blessed them and gave us a bright, pleased smile . . . We thought this the greatest event of our lives."

The Hotel d'Angleterre was the O'Connors' headquarters in Rome and it was a favorite stop for clergymen and California acquaintances. Besides Bishop Keane, a frequent visitor was Father Bernard John Vaughan, S.J., an eloquent speaker who gave Lenten sermons at the English Church in Rome. "He was a genial person who quite won our hearts," Mrs. O'Connor commented.

The seventy-three-year-old judge encountered the closest brush with death since his forty-niner days during a crosstown carriage ride in London on May 1, 1896. The couple was en route from an inn to the station over a rough street when O'Connor arose to open the window. The carriage lurched and he was flung violently against the door.

"I'll never forget that horrible moment," his wife wrote. "My first reaction and thought was to see if the door was fast. If it hadn't been locked, it would have been pushed open and certain death the result."

The O'Connors' final trip to Europe took place in 1899-1900, with much of the time being spent in their beloved Eternal City. "It would seem to me that life would have no charm after you have seen Rome for the last time," she underlined.

But life and charm have many facets, the O'Connors were to discover amid the harvest of their numerous benefactions.

St. Joseph's Catholic Church in 1888. The first church in San Jose, it was founded in 1803. Fire and earthquakes ravaged the old structure and the above building, which still stands, was dedicated in 1877. Parishioner Myles P. O'Connor provided the heating system and the organ and refinished the dome.

(Courtesy of San Jose Historic Landmarks Commission)

CHAPTER FOUR

A Place in the Country

THE STACCATO sounds of hammer and saw punctuated the valley air in the late Eighties as Judge O'Connor's rising new edifice typified a surge of new construction.

Times were good as the census taker counted twenty-one thousand persons in San José. The county's three other incorporated cities registered nine thousand and the rural community matched the cities with thirty thousand noses of its own. Passing poets searched for proper phrases to describe the idyllic scene as four million fruit trees and twenty-five thousand cattle dotted the valleys and foothills.

In San José, dirt streets cross-hatched the business district. A giant, 208-foot-high tower spreadeagled the intersection of Market and Santa Clara Streets, illuminating the downtown area for blocks in all directions. (The tower, erected in 1881 as the largest of its kind in California, served its purpose well until high winds toppled it in 1915). From the tower, one could look northeast past Tenth Street and see mustard fields tall and rank all the way to Alum Rock.

The valley boasted of producing half the world's supply of prunes and garden seed. It claimed the largest Angora goat herds on the globe. Its quicksilver mines were said to be the richest anywhere. Alviso talked of its vast oyster beds, Evergreen cattlemen rated their herds second to none and Uvas Creek farmers cultivated row upon row of leafy tobacco plants.

There was never any question that Theodore Lenzen would be the O'Connors' choice as architect for the sanitarium. The Prussian-born Lenzen was a busy man in this era, planning the City Hall in the Market Street plaza and the fortress-like Fredericksburg Brewery on The Alameda. The City Hall, the Vendome Hotel and the O'Connor Sanitarium all opened their doors in 1889. Lenzen had come to San Francisco in 1861 and when only 28 years

O'Connor Sanitarium under construction in 1888. Designed by architect Theodore Lenzen, it opened in the spring of 1889 although a few doorknobs were still missing and the kitchen was without a stove.

(Courtesy of San Jose Historic Landmarks Commission)

of age had drawn up plans for St. Ignatius College (now University of San Francisco). The Jesuits recommended Lenzen to Santa Clara College and he designed many of the buildings there.

Judge O'Connor picked a site for the sanitarium that in those days was well out in the country. Measuring 8.395 acres, it was located south of Stevens Creek Road between Meridian Road and Race Street. The sanitarium (hospital being somewhat of a distasteful word in those days) was "situated in one of the finest parts of the valley and is destined to be a much frequented spot," predicted the *San José Herald*.

The building had been under construction a year when Sister Severina Brandel arrived on February 22, 1889, in San Francisco from her former post in raucous Virginia City, Nevada. Sister Severina, appointed as the first superior, found that only the first floor was ready for occupancy at the sanitarium and she returned to San Francisco to live at an orphanage while she awaited arrival of three other members of her order, the Daughters of Charity of St. Vincent de Paul, from the motherhouse in Emmitsburg, Maryland.

The O'Connors' choice of the Daughters of Charity to run the institution was not by chance. The order, founded by St. Vincent de Paul and Louise de Marillac, had an long and honorable record of service. Its first members were twelve French peasant girls who assembled in Paris in 1633 under the roof of a widow of noble birth who later was canonized as Sainte Louise de Marillac. This was the first uncloistered religious community of women. Others had been tried without success. The founders wanted the sisters to move about freely in society, succoring the poor and destitute. They took simple vows, repeating them each year on the Feast of the Annunciation. And still today, they adhere to the wishes of St. Vincent, living with "no enclosure, but obedience; no grate but the fear of God; no veil, but holy modesty."

Voltaire wrote of the order:

"Perhaps there is nothing greater on earth than the sacrifice which a delicate sex makes of beauty, youth, and often high birth, to relieve in hospitals that gathering of human miseries of which the sight is so humiliating to pride and so revolting to our delicacy."

In America, the order was established by Elizabeth Bayley Seton. Born in a cultured, well-to-do New York family in 1774 as the Revolution brewed around her, she

A rear view of O'Connor Sanitarium in 1889 a few weeks after its completion. Constructed by Charles W. Denny, the building cost more than $300,000.

(Courtesy of San Jose Historic Landmarks Commission)

grew up to marry in wealth and position and bear five children. Then, her world was pulled from under her and within five years she lost her father, sister and husband—and her money. Mrs. Seton became a Catholic convert during her years of tragedy and in 1809 founded the religious community at Emmitsburg, Maryland. It was more than 40 years later, after Mother Seton's death, that her American community was formally affiliated with the French Daughters of Charity.

In its first three hundred years, the order blossomed to a world membership of forty-five thousand. The sisters operated schools, hospitals, orphanages, infant homes, sanitariums for the mentally ill and residences for working girls and the aged in more than 50 nations. They even administer the United States National Leprosarium in Carville, Louisiana, the only federal institution in the country operated by a religious order.

Joseph Sadoc Alemany, San Francisco's first archbishop, stopped at Emmitsburg in 1850 in an attempt to interest the sisters in spiritually destitute California. Cholera had orphaned hundreds of children in San Francisco and help was needed. In 1852, seven sisters left Emmitsburg for California via the Isthmus of Panama. Two of them, Sisters Ignatia and Honorine, died of cholera while crossing the tangled, steamy Panama jungles by foot and donkey. But the others pushed on and the order became firmly rooted in California soil.

The *San José Daily Herald* was intrigued by coming of the Daughters of Charity, especially by their habit, and informed readers on April 15, 1889:

"They wear a distinctive dress. Their broad white headdress is unlike anything

The pump house was an example of the self-sufficiency of the O'Connor Sanitarium. It is shown shortly after completion in 1889. In later years, the sanitarium grounds also provided fresh vegetables, fruit, eggs and milk for patients.

(Courtesy of San Jose Historical Landmarks Commission)

worn by the members of other orders. It has wings on the side more than a foot wide. It was adopted so that wounded soldiers might more easily distinguish the sisters in the smoke of the battle-field. They wear plain gray serge habits, with wide heavy sleeves. A wide white cape is worn over the shoulder and its ends extend nearly to the waist."

41

More accurately, the headdress was patterned after that worn by seventeenth century Norman peasants. But in 1964 the symbolic old habit was modernized, with a short bonnet or *coiffe* replacing the starched cornette. Drip-dry fabrics, shorter hemlines and narrower sleeves became the vogue.

On May 1, 1889, four sisters quietly moved into their new home. Sister Severina, the superior, had been joined by Sister Mary Oberdrifter, Sister Benedicta Tierney and Sister Aloysia Bowling. Of the four, three were trained nurses and one a housekeeper. The sisters found door knobs missing and the kitchen minus a range, but the discomforts were soon overcome.

The two-story building was built of brick, with sandstone facings, in an unadorned but handsome style. Giant white columns supported the portico over the main entrance, breaking up the monotony of the front profile. North and south wings stretched toward Meridian Road. The edifice was wisely divided into five compartments, each separated by thick brick walls. Doorways through the walls were made of iron covered by redwood so that in case of fire the flames might be confined to one compartment. The south wing's lower floor was a women's ward and the upper story the sisters' residence. The north wing housed the men's ward, store rooms and kitchen, with the second floor divided into apartment suites for families. In all, there were forty-four rooms and five wards. The basement contained the engine room, furnace and laundry. Halls and large rooms were heated by steam while smaller rooms had grates. The building was lighted by gas manufactured on the premises.

Theodore Lenzen, one of San Jose's most famous architects. Besides O'Connor Sanitarium, he also designed the City Hall, the Fredericksburg Brewery (now Falstaff) and buildings at Santa Clara College, College of Notre Dame and San Jose Normal School.

"The first patient admitted was a Protestant gentlemen from Santa Clara stricken with tuberculosis," the *San José Mercury* reported. "A room was hurriedly furnished and Mrs. J. J. Devine took him to the sanitarium in her carriage as the sisters had no means of transportation."

The O'Connors' original intent was for the sanitarium to serve as a home for the aged and needy. But their scope was so all-encompassing that at times they considered the institution as a health retreat, a winter resort for invalids and even as a branch of Father Kneipp's hydrotherapy movement. The *San José Herald* probably best summarized the situation:

"Mr. O'Connor's idea in founding the

I assure you it is very, very annoying to us both and to Mr. O'Connor it is very hurtful for him to be thus annoyed in the middle of his course — or "cure" here. Mr. Lenzen is a good Architect, but his judgment in such matters is not good. The fences, or rather the gates can soon be changed. Mr. O'C. has telegraphed to Mr. Lenzen to not commence the Walks & drives until he gets a letter — though Mr. L said he would not begin anything until he heard from us. But, as he has done so many things differently from what he said. We feared he might begin before receiving a letter if he did not telegraph —

Writing from Europe in 1889, Mrs. Myles O'Connor is upset with architect Theodore Lenzen over his landscape drawings for the new Sanitarium. Her husband was undergoing a "water cure" at a Czechoslovakian resort at the time.

The ornate wooden mantlepiece which O'Connor brought from Europe for his palatial San Jose home at Second and Reed Streets. The $40,000 residence was turned over to the Sisters of Notre Dame for an orphanage in 1894 and stands today on the Notre Dame High School campus.

institution was that it should be a place for the care of those who are well enough to leave a hospital, or not ill enough to enter one."

The O'Connors, who were touring Europe at the time of the sanitarium's completion, fought several bouts with the architect by mail over his deviations from their master plan.

The sanitarium well could have cut itself off from the outside world and had little trouble surviving. An artesian well on the site provided the water. A Mrs. Jordan donated chickens, C. T. Ryland and Bernard Murphy a horse and harness, McLaughlin a carriage and other friends offered cows and pigs. Fresh vegetables and fruits were grown on the grounds.

"We're happy to hear the radishes are growing," Mrs. O'Connor joked from Rome. "My husband—I fear—couldn't eat them [because of a stomach ailment]. They would be followed by many doses of bicarbonate."

Construction prices had a way of snowballing then as now. Judge O'Connor had agreed to put one hundred thousand dollars into the sanitarium, with the sisters to make it a paying operation thereafter. But the income at first was small and the O'Connors found that in a few years they had exceeded their original expenditure by three times. The judge agreed to pay the salaries of the hired hands, plus fifteen dollars a month to each sister, for the first year or until the sanitarium was in the black. The number of patients reached twelve by September, but mostly they were elderly guests, or "homers" as they were called.

The O'Connors were always on the lookout to help the needy. They sponsored the admission of an Ann Morrison and

Daughters of Charity, resplendent in their old-style cornettes, attend Mass in the St. Matthew's Memorial Chapel at O'Connor Sanitarium. The chapel was erected for $29,000 in 1892 by Myles P. O'Connor in memory of his brother, Matthew, who was killed in the War with Mexico. Paintings and statuary were brought by the O'Connors from Europe.

later a Sister Polycarp. Typical of Mrs. O'Connor was an incident in October, 1890, when she saw an old man hobbling from St. Joseph's Church. She persuaded him to take a room at the sanitarium. He died three months later. "I am glad," she said in a note to the sisters, "that at least we were able to make his last days comfortable and happy."

The institution's slow start was due in part to the lack of publicity of its facilities. The *San José Herald* on November 4, 1889, apologetically discussed the sanitarium in an editorial: "There must be hundreds of sick people in this and adjoining counties who should be only too glad to take advantage of its benefits . . . Of course, it has not been open for patients

An etched glass door imported from Europe by Myles O'Connor in the 1880s. It is located in the former O'Connor residence at Second and Reed Streets, San Jose, now occupied by the Sisters of Notre Dame.

so very long, but as far as the *Herald* is concerned, it will be more frequently mentioned."

A flow of furnishings from abroad soon transformed the sanitarium into a place of elegance. Canaries chirped from swinging cages in the lobby, heavy red Brussels carpets lined the wide corridors and oil paintings and statuary were everywhere.

Many of the paintings were hung in St. Matthew's Memorial Chapel, built in the south wing in 1892 as a personal gift of Judge O'Connor in honor of his deceased brother. The twenty-nine thousand dollar chapel seated 264. It contained fourteen stained glass windows made in Munich. The woodwork was of valuable Circassian walnut.

The sanitarium offered no surgery, no maternity, no laboratory, no pediatric and no emergency department in its formative years. Yet it won the respect of the community, principally because of the tender touch of the Daughters of Charity.

The *San Francisco Monitor*, on April 2, 1893, related one incident:

"A deputy at the San José City Hall was taken ill, and after persuasion, consented to be treated at the magnificent Home provided through Myles O'Connor. He regained his health in time and said, 'I have been a rabid anti-Catholic for thirty-five years, but five weeks at the Sanitarium has wrought a wonderful change in me. I never knew there were such ministering angels on earth as the sisters I found there. I see life in new light. Now, and hereafter, my voice will be raised in praise of those blessed women.' "

In 1894, the O'Connors decided they wanted to be closer to their sanitarium. They gave their forty thousand dollar home at Second and Reed streets to the Sisters of Notre Dame for a girls orphanage, with accommodations of up to fifty youngsters. On St. Patrick's Day, the judge named it the Notre Dame Institute. Later, he provided eighteen thousand dollars more for the orphans' education. Taking charge of the institute was Sister

46

Caretakers work in front of O'Connor Sanitarium in this 1889 view looking east. Race Street, a dirt thoroughfare, is seen between the two fences.

(Courtesy of San Jose Historic Landmarks Commission)

Mary Theresa of Jesus, a descendant of a famous family. She was the niece of pioneer Californian General Mariano G. Vallejo, and the great-great-granddaughter of explorer and San Francisco Bay discoverer, Don Gaspar de Portola. Again off for Europe, the O'Connors left plans for construction of a new residence to be attached to the south wing of the sanitarium. They occupied it in 1895 and it served them the rest of their lives.

By the end of the century, medicine was advancing in giant strides. Doctors were treating patients at O'Connor's Sanitarium in growing numbers. An expanding community was making demands and the sanitarium responded. Sister Raphael Jones, the second superior, began the moves that would change the institution from a sleepy home for the elderly to a full-fledged hospital. She ordered the Brussels carpets rolled up and sanitary flooring installed. Rocking chairs came out of the rooms. High hospital beds went in. Electricity replaced the old acetylene lighting system, which for years would go off nightly at nine o'clock to leave the nurses and patients with only candlelight until morning. Sister Raphael had moved to push back the darkness.

CHAPTER FIVE

Doctors on Horseback

While O'Connor Sanitarium was pioneering in the hospital field in the Central Coast region in California, the practice of medicine already was well established.

Actually, the medical art in California reached back as far as April 29, 1769, when Dr. Pedro Prat—a captain in the Royal Spanish Army who became first surgeon general at the Monterey Presidio—alighted in San Diego.

The trip from La Paz in Baja California had been tragic. Two-thirds of the passengers on the two ships, the *San Carlos* and the *San Antonio,* died en route from dysentery and scurvy. A third ship, the *San José,* was lost at sea and never heard from again. Dr. Prat set up a shore hospital to care for the ailing. But the ordeal drained him physically and he died within two years at Monterey.

Each California mission had its hospital, a lone room with mats on the floor. The padres kept medical-surgical kits, and one still is preserved at Mission San Juan Bautista.

Caesarian sections were performed by the Franciscan friars. One was recorded in San Francisco in 1805 and another in the San José Pueblo in 1825. In 1812, Dr. Manuel Quix performed California's first autopsy on the body of Padre Andres Quintana, who had been slain by a berserk Indian at the Santa Cruz Mission.

A Harvard graduate named John Marsh, who had had some medical training in Min-

Dr. Benjamin Cory, the first physician to settle and practice in Santa Clara Valley. Dr. Cory arrived in 1847 and combined careers in mining, public service and medicine.

nesota, came to Los Angeles in 1836. By some fast talking, he convinced Mexican authorities the Latin on his Harvard diploma signified his medical degree, and he was licensed to practice. Marsh later moved into the hills east of Mt. Diablo in the present Alameda County. But his eccentric demeanor and extremely high medical fees made him thoroughly disliked. The first non-military doctor to come to California via Monterey was Edward Turner Bale in 1837. His medical credentials also were suspect. But Bale married into General Vallejo's family and was granted property near the present town of St. Helena. He took ill hunting gold in 1849 and died on his ranch. The famed Bale Mill, built in 1846, is still a tourist attraction 120 years later.

Dr. Nicholas Den, whose Norman forbears had gone to Ireland in 1171 in the retinue of Henry II, arrived in Santa Barbara in the late 1830's. Although he had had some medical training, his interests were more in public service. His brother, Dr. Richard Somerset Den, joined him on September 1, 1843. Richard, a graduate of the University of Dublin, practiced thirty-four years in Santa Barbara and Los Angeles and was California's first foreign physician possessing a medical degree. The Dens' accomplishments are well-chronicled in the archives of Nicholas' granddaughter, Mrs. Henry L. Warburton of Santa Clara.

John Townsend, the first American M.D. to settle in California, was a man whose life was marked by high adventure and stark tragedy. He crossed the plains in the Stevens-Murphy-Townsend Party in 1844.

Martin Murphy was the Irish-born patriarch who settled on an 8,927-acre spread and built an adobe homestead at the foot of the peak that today overlooks the city of Morgan Hill. The community was titled after a man named Hill who married Murphy's daughter, Diana, not for the nearby peak, which is actually El Toro, or sometimes Murphy's Peak. The village of San Martin grew up around the chapel erected on the rancho of one of Murphy's sons.

Another of the patriarch's sons, Bernard, was of great assistance to Myles O'Connor in opening of his San José sanitarium. By 1884, the year O'Connor moved to the Santa Clara Valley, the Murphy dynasty had holdings of three million acres in California, Arizona and Nevada. Captain Elisha Stevens, whose name is perpetuated by a creek, reservoir and major thoroughfare in Santa Clara Valley, was a frontiersman who settled near Cupertino until "too much durn civilization" chased him into the desert near Bakersfield. This heroic party was the first to bring wagons over the Sierra.

Dr. Townsend, a true doctor-adventurer, went to Monterey and then to Yerba Buena where he was the first physician to open an office. From April to October, 1848, he was the town's superior alcalde (mayor).

John Townsend, the first American M.D. to settle in California, was a member of the famous Stevens-Murphy-Townsend Party of 1844. Dr. Townsend practiced in San Francisco and then moved to an adobe two miles north of San Jose where he and his wife died of cholera in 1849.

(Courtesy of San Jose Historic Landmarks Commission)

He also was a school trustee and a real estate promoter, Townsend Street bearing his name. Dr. Townsend made a trip to the Sierra gold fields, but he was back in San Francisco in 1849. The turmoil of the city proved distasteful and he decided to move to a country adobe two miles north of San José. A cholera epidemic swept into Northern California the next year, affecting the San José pueblo where an estimated ten per cent of the population perished. San Francisco counted 500 dead in three months alone. Dr. Townsend, battling the disease with the meager medicinal weapons at his command, died of cholera in December. Twenty-four hours later, his wife followed him in death. Their lives had been marked by hardship; their dreams of a quiet life in the country went unfilled.

A grim coincidence laced the Townsend story. The doctor's wife, Elizabeth Louise, was the sister of Moses Schallenberger. Moses was six years old when he was left an orphan in Ohio and the Townsends took him in. Moses later accompanied the Townsends in their historic trek to California. When Dr. and Mrs. Townsend died from cholera in 1850, their two-year-old son was left an orphan. Schallenberger, with a sudden chance to repay the Townsends for their earlier beneficence, assumed charge of the boy. As John Henry Moses Townsend, he grew up to become a prominent farmer, and a state legislator in 1883. In his boyhod, he was cared for awhile by the sisters at Notre Dame Convent in San José and he often was teased as being the first alumnus of the girls' school, the College of Notre Dame.

Schallenberger moved from the Townsend estate in 1856, buying an adjacent 120 acres near the intersection of Coyote

James Manning Cory, co-discoverer of the famed Esmeralda Mine in Western Nevada. Joining him in staking the claim was his brother, Dr. Benjamin Cory, San Jose's first practicing physician.

(Courtesy of Clyde Arbuckle)

Residence of Dr. Benjamin Cory, 435 South Second Street, San Jose. Erected during the Civil War in 1864, it was more than 80 years old when it was torn down.

(Courtesy of Clyde Arbuckle)

River and San José-Milpitas Road. Schallenberger's daughter became Mrs. Margaret Schallenberger McNaught, an early Commissioner of Elementary Schools in California. Another daughter, Louise, married T. S. Montgomery, who built the Montgomery and Sainte Claire Hotels and on July 6, 1933, gave the City of San José the property for the new Civic Auditorium.

But Schallenberger is best recognized by history for his link with the Donner Party. While accompanying Dr. Townsend westward in 1844, Moses agreed with two companions to stay and guard a large supply of goods cached near a lake (Donner Lake) while the rest of the party pushed on through the snowy mountains. The trio built a cabin and planned to live off game until spring. But little did they know their camp site was located in one of the world's heaviest snow belts. Soon, they were compelled to fashion snowshoes out of barrel staves and try to make it over the mountains. They hadn't gone far when Schallenberger, a gawky lad of seventeen, collapsed of fatigue. He persuaded his companions to go on without him. Somehow he managed to stagger back to the cabin. He was so exhausted he had to reach down and lift his feet over the nine-inch doorsill. His courage was severely taxed over the long winter, but he trapped foxes and coyotes for food and kept up his spirits by reading books, including some medical texts left by Dr. Townsend. Marooned in the wilds, Moses in his own words later could describe the ordeal only as "miserable." His sister, Mrs. Townsend, pleaded with a member of the party, Dennis Martin, to rescue Schallenberger. Martin agreed and in late February, 1845, he found Schallenberger weak but alive in the near-buried cabin. This was the primitive dwelling that sheltered part of the Donner Party two winters later.

San José's first physician was Dr. Benjamin Cory, a bold Ohioan who drove an ox team over the Oregon Trail in 1847. Autumn rains soured him on the Northwest and he left by sea for California, arriving in Yerba Buena on his 25th birthday, November 17, 1847. It took only three weeks to convince him that this seaport was over-populated with doctors. Already established were John Townsend, Victor J. Fourgeaud, and the illustrious part-time editor who was to develop a craving for gold dust, Elbert P. Jones.

Cory heard of a pueblo forty miles south called San José, which had been founded in 1777 and was considered California's first real municipality. He journeyed to Alviso by sailboat, a sleepless, twenty-four hour trip over a turbulent bay. He traversed the last nine miles to San José on a bronco chartered from a Mexican for $1.50. Those were his last pennies. But he had his medical books, a supply of surgical equipment and drugs, and a community to himself.

Dr. Cory's first residence was Peter Davidson's place at Santa Clara and San Pedro Streets where the Farmer's Union store was located many years later. But Cory felt the $1.50 a day was too high and he moved to The Half Moon, San José's first hotel, operated by Zachariah Jones.

Cory made two sorties into the gold fields, the first with the bellowing Jones who was nicknamed "Buffalo" because of his voice. The mass of would-be miners was so great that Cory and Jones had to camp eleven days at the Carquinez Straits awaiting passage to the gold country. They went to Mormon Island on the American River's south fork and soon re-

Zachariah Jones, nicknamed "Buffalo" because of his roaring voice, accompanied Dr. Benjamin Cory on one trip to the gold "diggings." Jones operated The Half Moon, San Jose's first hotel. He also opened the area's first sawmill.

(Courtesy of Clyde Arbuckle)

turned with tales of the riches there. Cory's next trip was made with Robert Neligh, an agent for Commodore Robert F. Stockton. Travelers reported seeing them panning gold on the Stanislaus River and Neligh was said to have sacked away $2,000 in gold dust in three months.

The pair split up and on November 6, 1848, Dr. Cory wrote a letter to his brother, James Manning Cory, describing his life in the gold fields. Dr. Cory was fascinated with mining, an avocation he pursed all his life. But his medical diploma

was difficult to hide and miners were calling on him day and night. He told his brother of riding seventy-five miles to see a rancher dying from an infection caused by a rifle ball in his arm. Dr. Cory deftly made an incision, removed the ball and the patient recovered. "Charge me what you want," the rancher said. "Here is my ranch, with its horses and cattle. And I have a large bag of gold." Cory took a small fee and then confided to his brother: "I wish I didn't have that 'Doctor' stuck to my name. I am vexed to death. My conscience will not permit me to charge much to my patients."

The doctor devised ingenious plans to deter the constant interruptions in his quest of a gold strike. For a while, he told patients he was negligent, completely irresponsible and would make a call only with great reluctance. "Now, they pester me more than ever," he sighed. On another occasion Cory wrote that his next tack was to carry with him ample medicine, but "charge abundantly" for his services. "A minimum fee will be a half-ounce of gold." Just how this plan worked never was disclosed, but his friends reported Cory's threats always evaporated whenever an ailing soul rapped on his tent door.

The physician was said to have taken home $4,000 in gold dust to San José. He was a generous and carefree man who never attained great wealth because of his propensity for lending it to friends who took their time repaying it. He also had a habit of telling patients to "pay me when you can," and to many this was never. Once a Sacramento acquaintance wrote and asked him for a $700 loan. Cory intuitively felt the fellow a bad risk and refused him. The acquaintance wrote again and his hard luck story won over the doc-

California's first capitol, which was built in San Jose through the efforts of such men as Dr. Benjamin Cory and Dr. John Townsend. Meeting in this statehouse was the "Legislature of One Thousand Drinks."

(Courtesy of Clyde Arbuckle)

tor. Cory authorized a $700 note, with the Sacramento man to pay it back to the bank on fixed terms. Some time later, the bank notified Cory that the acquaintance had not met the loan and the doctor must pay it. Cory was furious. He wrote a harsh letter to the borrower, ending it with the exclamation: "Furthermore, you are no gentleman!"

A week later, a representative of the Sacramentoan banged on Dr. Cory's office door, bearing a challenge to a duel. "You have a choice of weapons," declared the stranger. The stunned Cory sat back and began to laugh. "Shotguns—at ten paces," he said. The stranger frowned. Cory insisted, "Shotguns at ten paces—take it or leave it." The stranger left. A few days later the note was quietly paid up and Cory never heard of the incident again.

Cory would go on horseback where roads were absent and he was sometimes away from his office a week on distant calls. The silhouette of a solitary horseman, his shiny black hat glittering in the moonlight as he rode through the oaks, was a familiar Santa Clara Valley sight. He would sing hymns as he rode and was

known as "The Singing Doctor." He was especially loved by the Spanish-speaking residents and it was said that half of the babies born in those days were baptized Benjamin in the physician's honor.

Once in the late 1850's, Dr. Cory was called to Alviso. After the treatment, the patient boasted of his rich marshland crops and gave the doctor a giant L-shaped sweet potato as a sample. Dr. Cory was en route home at dusk when a highwayman leaped from the bushes and ordered him to throw down his money and valuables. As the man advanced, Dr. Cory unconsciously picked up the sweet potato from the buggy seat and began twiddling it in his hands. The robber stopped, peered through the darkness and then suddenly threw up his arms. "Don't shoot!" he shrieked. He then leaped into the underbrush and disappeared. Cory didn't realize what had happened for a few minutes. The highwayman had been in no mood for a "gun" battle.

When Dr. Cory came to San José, it consisted of a few adobes clustered around the Plaza. He gambled the village would grow and prosper, but little did he think that three years later it would become Cali-

53

fornia's first state capital. Among the most active workers in bringing the capital to San José were two doctors—Cory and John Townsend.

"Often one will find that the best-educated, the most forward-looking, the most constructive citizen in a town, the man who gets things done for the good of the community, is a physician," Dr. Walter C. Alvarez, the noted medical newspaper columnist who interned in San Francisco's City-County Hospital, once wrote.

He could not have more aptly described Benjamin Cory. At twenty-eight, he was a member of California's first legislative assembly. He was a city councilman for four years, a city board of education member for one term, a San José State Normal School trustee for ten years, and the guiding force in the founding of Santa Clara County Hospital.

After San José's selection as the capital site, the city underwent hectic days trying to make good on its promises.

Author Bayard Taylor graphically described the community as he found it in the fall of 1850:

"The two weeks which had elapsed since San José had been made a capital were sufficient to have created a wonderful change. What with tents thrown up, the town seemed to have doubled in size. The dusty streets were thronged with people; goods for lack of storage room, stood in large piles beside the doors; the sound of saw and hammer, the rattling of laden carts, were incessant. The legislative building, a two-story adobe house built at the town's expense, was nearly finished. Hotels were springing up in all quarters; French restaurateurs hung out their signs on little, one-story shanties; the Celestials [Chinese] had already planted themselves

there, and summoned men to meals by the sound of their barbaric gongs."

During its two years as capital, San José was constantly criticized for its lack of facilities. Monterey residents guffawed that going to San José was "moving from the habitation of man to the land of the coyotes."

San José still was relatively isolated, served only by stagecoaches. The forty-five mile ride to San Francisco took ten hours and the fare was two ounces of gold. Travelers coming by sea arrived in Alviso. They often had to slosh through nine miles of mud to San José. Stock was offered for sale to finance a $100,000 plank road over this distance. Dr. Cory was one of nineteen San Joséans, or "puebloans" as they were called by defamers, who raised $34,000 to build the first statehouse. When opponents urged the capital be moved, citizens doubled their efforts to keep it. Dr. Townsend offered 200 acres as a site for the new buildings. But in less than two years, the fight was over. San José had lost its capital to Vallejo, Benicia and finally Sacramento. San Joséans never gave up hope of regaining it and in 1893 a resolution passed the Legislature to return the capital to its original location. But the State Supreme Court adjudged the resolution illegal and issued an injunction forbidding a proposition on the ballot.

Dr. Cory's office on the Plaza was believed a common meeting place for state legislators before the statehouse was completed. City officials dropped by, too. Dr. Cory was appointed to a position that, in effect, made him the city's first health officer. The saying at that time was that "more good government came out of Dr. Cory's office than out of both houses of the State Legislature and the City Hall put together."

Although the first lawmaking body was as productive as any in the state's history, it found itself later called the "Legislature of One Thousand Drinks." There are about as many accounts of the title's origin as there were drinks, but one fact weaves through them all—the lawmakers were not teetotalers.

The Cory name became part of Nevada history when the physician's brother, James Manning Cory, and several partners discovered the great Esmeralda silver and gold mine near Mono Lake in 1860. James Manning Cory, who named the mine after a character in Victor Hugo's "The Hunchback of Notre Dame," made $30,000 from his investment. Dr. Cory, whose name appeared on the first claim along with that of Josiah Belden, the first mayor of San José, realized a smaller fortune.

Cory's penchant for mining lingered on and he later made lengthy trips to Durango, Mexico, to invest in a silver mine. His enthusiasm attracted other San José investors, but the mine was a financial flop.

The physician was known for his good humor and love of practical jokes. His grandson, Benjamin Cory Ledyard, a well-known dentist in San José for a half-century who is now retired, remembers when Dr. Cory once went riding with his son, Louis. "See that jackrabbit," the doctor said to the boy, who was to become an eminent Fresno lawyer and real estate developer. "Watch me hit him right in the eye." The boy frowned in disbelief since the rabbit was a good distance away in a marshy field. Cory drew his sidearm and fired. The boy retrieved the rabbit, gasping that the shot was as accurate as the doctor had predicted. "Of course," Dr. Cory said

jauntily, although he was even more amazed at his feat than his son.

The popular physician practiced forty-nine years. His partner late in his career was Dr. William D. McDougall, a former New Yorker who came to the forefront when he was appointed city smallpox physician during the 1887-1888 scare in San José. Dr. Cory lived in a magnificent home at 435 South Second Street. He gradually withdrew from practice and died January 16, 1896. Death was attributed to "starvation." Dr. McDougall told the *San José Mercury* that Cory's stomach refused to take food the last six months. At the time illness forced him from his office, he had been in practice longer than any physician on the Pacific Coast. Eight children survived him. An avenue and an elementary school perpetuate his name.

Close on Cory's heels came Santa Clara's premier physician, Dr. Henry Hulme Warburton. Born in Staffordshire, England, he was one of seven brothers who were doctors. Their father also was a physician. Dr. Warburton studied and practiced under his father for seven years before he came to New York in 1844. He practiced there a year and then signed on as a surgeon on a whaler, the *Corea*, in New London, Connecticut. He resigned this rather arduous post and, when the ship docked at Half Moon Bay in 1847, he went to Woodside on the San Francisco Peninsula. He moved to a residence near the Santa Clara Mission in 1848 and, except for a fling in the gold fields, he practiced medicine until his death at the age of eighty-three.

Dr. Warburton is recognized as Santa Clara's first medical man, although a Dr. James C. Isbel wintered at the Mission in 1846-1847. However, Isbel did not practice. His wife, Olive, a niece of educator

Dr. Henry Hulme Warburton, pioneer physician who came to the Santa Clara Valley in 1848. At his death in 1903, he had been practicing 56 years—longer than any physician on the Pacific Coast.

(Courtesy of San Jose Historic Landmarks Commission)

Horace Mann, is said to have taught the first English school in the valley during that spring of 1847.

Dr. Warburton's practice extended into Washington and Oregon territories where he occasionally called on patients and, like Dr. Cory, he was much revered by all who knew him. Mrs. Mary Den Warburton, the doctor's daughter-in-law whose great-grandfather was José Francisco Ortega, a scout of Portola's expedition in 1779, passes on the oft-told family story of a trip Dr. Warburton took into the country south of San José in the 1850's. Dr. Warburton apparently wandered into the hide-out of a bandit, believed to be the legendary Joaquin Murietta. Murietta was about

to shoot Dr. Warburton when one of the brigand's lieutenants recognized the doctor as the man who had saved his child from death by diptheria some time before. Murietta agreed to spare the visitor if he would promise not to tell the location of the hideout. The physician was all too happy to cooperate.

Dr. Warburton attended the Vasquez family in Santa Clara many times. When the notorious bandit, Tiburcio Vasquez, was wounded and caught in Southern California in 1874, he was brought to San José. Minutes after he was hanged, the Vasquez family implored Dr. Warburton to try to mend the bandit's broken neck in hopes his life might be saved.

Dr. Warburton was short of stature and wore a skullcap in making his rounds. In 1870, he visited his native England and was received like a prodigal son. While there, he was successful in encouraging his brother to come to California. Dr. James P. Warburton maintained his practice in San Francisco and Alameda for many years. At his death in February, 1903, Dr. Henry Warburton had been in practice fifty-six years, the longest of any physician on the West Coast and was still treating patients the day he died. Despite a heavy cold, he went out in the rain on a call. As he was returning he collapsed and expired before a doctor could reach him.

Flags were flown at half-staff on the Santa Clara College campus where Dr. Warburton had been the physician for many years. His daily ledgers and instruments are in the possession of a grandson, Austen D. Warburton, a San José attorney.

Twenty-one years after his death, his was still a potent name in Santa Clara medicine. In 1924, a man brought a prescription into a Santa Clara drug store and asked the pharmacist to refill it. The pharmacist was surprised when he noticed the original prescription was written fifty-seven years before in 1867 by Dr. Warburton. It was dutifully filled and the man went on his way without blinking an eye.

The medical men who came to the Santa Clara Valley immediately after Cory and Warburton were reacting to the stimulus of gold, climate or opportunity in a growing new land. And the doctors who had traded scalpels for gold pans soon had scalpels in their hands again. Dr. John P. Dudley came in November, 1850; Dr. A. B. Caldwell, 1851, and Drs. A. J. Spencer, Arthur Wellsley Saxe, Benjamin F. Headen and Benjamin Bryant, 1852. They were closely followed by Drs. G. B. Crane, William Seifert and T. D. Johnson.

Dr. Dudley, who traced his ancestry to the Massachusetts Bay Colony, studied medicine at Buffalo University, which was then directed by the politically ambitious Millard Fillmore. During his long practice, he lived on a 200-acre ranch five miles south of San José on Almaden Road. He and Benjamin Cory's brother, Andrew Jackson Cory, formed a local militia to fight on the Union side, if necessary, during the Civil War. His hobby was tinkering in his shop where he invented and patented a horseshoe which equalized the bearing on hooves.

Dr. A. B. Caldwell is remembered for his opening in 1848 of Caldwell's Upper Store, which sold supplies to the miners and was the first house built in Nevada City. His son, Robert, attended Santa Clara College and then signed on as a surgeon for the Western Union Telegraph Company party that laid the Pacific cable reaching to Siberia in the 1860's. Robert Caldwell formalized his medical education

Dr. John P. Dudley, an 1850 arrival in Santa Clara Valley. His frame ranch home at Robertsville on Almaden Road has been an area landmark for many years.

at the University of Californa, then traveled widely through the Orient. He once was a ship's physician on Japan's Inland Sea. He had been practicing in Nagasaki for four years when A. B. Caldwell died in San José in 1876. Robert then returned to take over his father's practice.

Dr. Alexander J. Spencer's arrival in 1852 marked the beginning of a span of public service and personal accomplishment equalled by few families in San José history. Coming from upper New York State, Dr. Spencer crossed the plains in a wagon train and was part of the Gold Rush in 1849 until illness forced him to return to the East. But one icy winter there was enough and the physician returned with his family in a wagon train in 1852.

Charles Henry (Mountain Charley) Mc-Kiernan, well-known San Jose businessman in the late 19th century. He always wore a hat because of a large scar on his head, the result of an attack by a grizzly bear in the Santa Cruz Mountains in 1854. Dr. A. J. Spencer of San Jose later inserted a metal plate in McKiernan's skull in one of the first known operations of its kind in the West.

(Courtesy of San Jose Historic Landmarks Commission)

Dr. Spencer's meeting with Charles Henry (Mountain Charley) McKiernan is one of the most frequently repeated accounts of that era. Born in Ireland, McKiernan had been a teamster and lumberman until his twenty-five-mule team was run off by Indians in Humboldt County. The disheartened McKiernan then moved to the Santa Cruz Mountains where Indians were scarce. He was the first American to settle there and his expertness with a

gun enabled him to shoot and sell game in the more populous lowland areas.

Mountain Charley's encounter with a grizzly bear is legendary and no doubt some of the facts were lost in the retelling. But McKiernan evidently did tangle with a ferocious animal of some kind in the spring of 1854 and the frontiersman's scalp was badly torn. Bleeding badly and unconscious from a skull fracture, Mountain Charley was left for dead and friends who found him hours later held little hope for his survival as they rushed him to a physician. Dr. Thomas J. Ingersoll of San José patched him up. But McKiernan suffered blinding headaches until Dr. Spencer inserted a silver plate in his skull a year later. This was believed the first case of trephining in California. McKiernan lived another forty-eight years and became a respected San José businessman, dividing his time between his hay and grain firm and his vineyards. Dr. Spencer practiced thirty years in San José, retiring to Florida where he died at seventy-six in 1882. His oldest son, Francis E. Spencer, was a San José jurist. A second son, Hume A. Spencer, was one of the valley's first veterinarians.

Dr. A. J. Spencer's great-grandson is County Superior Court Judge Marshall S. Hall. Judge Hall's family is steeped in medicine. His father, J. Underwood Hall Jr., was the O'Connor Sanitarium's first staff physician and first president of the medical staff.

Dr. Spencer's associate for many years was Dr. Francis W. James, whose family was long in the forefront of valley history. Dr. James had come to the California gold country in 1850 in the company of a lifelong friend, Dr. William J. Knox. Dr. James then returned to his native Kentucky while Dr. Knox settled in Nevada City.

Dr. Benjamin F. Headen, pioneer physician who came to the Santa Clara Valley from Kentucky in 1852. He was instrumental in development of a medical school at the University of Pacific in San Jose, the first medical school to open in the Western states.

Dr. William J. Knox, eminent physician, state legislator and community builder in San Jose in the 1860s. His partner was Dr. Francis W. James, whose grandson, William, became a prominent Superior Court judge.

Dr. Knox persuaded Dr. James, then in Missouri, to return to California in 1860 when the James-Spencer medical partnership was formed in San José. Dr. Knox had been a state assemblyman from Nevada City. But in 1863, he moved to San José. Two years later, Dr. Knox made two significant moves. First, he ran for the State Senate and won. Second, he persuaded James Lick, donor of the Lick Observatory, to sell him property at the northwest corner of First and Santa Clara Streets, which a century later was occupied by the J. C. Penney Company.

Few buildings in San José history rate in importance with that of the Knox Block.

It was the city's most elegant building upon its completion. Dr. Knox and his brother-in-law, T. Ellard Beans, founded the city's first bank at this location in March, 1866, under the name of Knox and Beans. After a sudden illness proved fatal to Dr. Knox at the Lick House in San Francisco in 1867, the business was merged into and succeeded by the Bank of San José.

In 1847, Dr. James welcomed a grandson, William, into the family. He grew up to become Superior Court Judge William F. James, who was ninety at his retirement from the bench in 1964. He lives with his wife, Dr. Maude Merrill James, a Stanford

59

Santa Clara County Hospital shortly after its opening on a 114-acre site on San Jose-Los Gatos Road in 1875. Drs. Benjamin Cory and Andrew Jackson Cory led the campaign to built a new county medical facility.

(Courtesy of San Jose Mercury-News)

University psychologist, at their campus residence.

Dr. Arthur Wellsley Saxe, also a New Yorker, put in his time in the gold diggings before settling in Santa Clara. A skillful surgeon, he was elected president of the California State Medical Society in 1880 and served as a state senator in 1884. Dr. Saxe was interested in leprosy and he made a trip to Hawaii to study it. His report was esteemed by the State Medical Society. When Dr. Saxe retired to his garden where he grew more than 250 varieties of roses, his son, Frank K., assumed the medical practice. Their office was located at Benton and Main Streets.

Dr. Headen, a bearded Kentuckian, lived on a sixty-one-acre ranch on the edge of Santa Clara. His interest was centered in the University of the Pacific, a Methodist-Episcopalian institution in San José that gave birth in 1858 to the first medical school in the Far West. Dr. Elias Samuel Cooper, the best known of the early California surgeons, was instrumental in starting the school that later moved to San Francisco and bore his name. It eventually became Stanford Medical School. Dr. Headen was one of three physicians among the original seventeen medical school trustees. He served twenty years as a trustee and treasurer at the university which later moved to Stockton.

Benjamin Bryant was typical of the

Looking northeast from the intersection of First and Santa Clara Streets on a summer day in 1888 when San Jose celebrated opening of first electric street car service west of the Rocky Mountains. The cars had underground trolleys and pedestrians delighted in short-circuiting them with umbrellas. The big building is the Bank of San Jose, originally located across the street in the Knox Block (left) under the name of Knox and Beans. Founded in 1866 by Dr. William J. Knox and T. Ellard Beans, it was San Jose's first bank.

(Courtesy of San Jose Mercury-News)

doctor-adventurers of the 1850's. He came to San Francisco on June 12, 1849, helped establish a hospital in Sacramento, built a hotel in Yuba County and finally settled in Gilroy on November 20, 1852. That region would not support a physician so Dr. Bryant took to sheep raising. He later practiced medicine in San José.

Hospitals began appearing in California in the 1850's. Santa Clara County took action in 1854 to care for the sick, the Board of Supervisors appointing three of its members—George Peck, R. G. Moody and William Daniels—to study the problem. The County in 1855 set up a hospital in a house on Second Street and contracted for a physician. Dr. G. B. Crane agreed to see no more than seven patients a day for $4,600 a year. Then, Dr. A. B. Caldwell contracted to see them for $2.50 a day in 1857-1859. Dr. T. D. Johnson took over the task and carried on until the County in 1860 bought twelve acres at a cost of $333 an acre from Hiram Cahill to erect a hospital facility. The site was on the present Park Avenue near Montgomery Street. By 1868, it was obvious the facilities were too small. The County in 1871 acquired the present 114-acre site on Bascom Avenue. It was purchased from John S. O'Connor for $109 an acre, a reasonable sum in those days.

Again it was Dr. Benjamin Cory in the forefront, spearheading the campaign that convinced taxpayers a new hospital was a necessity. The $20,000 facility opened in 1875. It's first director was his brother, Dr. Andrew Jackson Cory. The Gothic-style, three-story building accommodated 115 patients, and sightseers came from afar. Historian J. P. Munro-Fraser, in melan-

Andrew Jackson Cory, brother of pioneer physician Benjamin Cory. Andrew Cory was the first director of the Santa Clara County Hospital opening in 1875. The Cory brothers led the campaign to build the Gothic-style, three-story structure.

(Courtesy of Clyde Arbuckle)

choly but flowery rhetoric, praised Ben Cory's campaigning and "the result was that a beautiful structure was erected, and everything conducive to the welfare of the waifs of humanity has been done, so that their sufferings may be assuaged and their pillows smoothed as they fall into the grave."

The early pioneer doctors were bold, fearless, hard-driving men who did their best with the meager medical facilities at hand. Many of them were community leaders as well. In one regard they stood out almost to the man—a sense of compassion for the sick.

62

CHAPTER SIX

Twentieth Century Physicians

The art of healing in the Santa Clara Valley's early days was far from an exact science. Without the wonder drugs and modern facilities of today, doctors had to depend much on "educated guesswork" for their diagnoses and treatment.

Charlatans and quacks advertised on barn roofs and in newspapers, promising to cure every sickness known to man. The public was all too willing to give any new remedy a try.

Slowly, California's physicians began to adopt newly discovered techniques and laboratory aids. Anesthesia and clinical thermometers were introduced in the 1850's. Hypodermic administration of drugs came in the Sixties, improved urinalysis techniques in the Seventies and fowl cholera vaccine in the Eighties. Micro-organisms were defined in 1874 and Listerian methods of fighting bacteria were first tried in 1879.

Surgeons started using rubber gloves in the Nineties. Operations that carried 80 per cent mortality rates during the Gold Rush became safe and routine by 1900. In 1895, a German professor named Wilhelm Conrad Roentgen developed the first X-ray apparatus. San José soon boasted some of the finest radiologists in California.

America made few inroads into Germany's domination of medicine during the 19th century. But San José did reap a harvest of German-born physicians who gave

Dr. Thomas Kelley was a Civil War veteran who marched to the sea with General Sherman. He practiced 35 years in San Jose, 16 in partnership with Dr. Benjamin Cory. He also was a San Jose Postmaster and campaigned in the Nineties for a new post office, the present City Library on Market Street.

the community a brand of medicine equal to almost any part of the country.

Early-day operations were newsworthy events. On April 18, 1877, the *San José Daily Herald* reported on its first page:

"Yesterday afternoon, Dr. Brown, assisted by Drs. Thorne, Caldwell and Kelley, performed the operation of cutting out a cancer from the lower lip of B. C. Horn of this city. The patient was put under the influence of chloroform during the trying ordeal. Cancer is generally supposed to be a hereditary disease. It has occasionally been seen in infants."

Nine physicians formed the Santa Clara

Dr. John S. Potts, who combined his medical practice with public service. He founded the San Jose Board of Trade, a forerunner of the Chamber of Commerce.

County Medical Society in a loose fashion on May 9, 1870. It was re-organized along formal lines by 12 doctors on August 12, 1876. Its objectives were not only to discuss developments in medicine, but as one contemporary historian put it, "to fight itinerant quacks, charlatans and mountebanks flourishing on credulous human nature." The county society took its first swipe at government medicine in the preamble of its original constitution.

The medical men who tacked up their shingles in the backwash of the Civil War were every bit as swashbuckling as their forty-niner predecessors. Among them was Dr. William S. McMurty, a Kentuckian who helped organize the company that fought in the War with Mexico as part of the Mississippi Rifles Regiment commanded by a colonel who would be heard from again, Jefferson Davis. Dr. McMurty was a Texas ranger, a California gold seeker in 1849, a quartz miner at Grass Valley, a Santa Cruz mountain lumberman, a state senator in 1863 and a Los Gatos physician after 1868. There was Dr. Thomas Kelley, an 1871 arrival from Illinois who had soldiered in the Union Army at Shiloh, Corinth and Vicksburg and had marched to the sea with General Sherman. He was wounded in the thigh in July, 1863, at Jackson, Miss. He opened practice in San José immediately after his graduation from Chicago's Rush Medical College.

Dr. Kelley was a partner of Dr. Benjamin Cory for 16 years, a San José postmaster under appointment of President Harrison in 1890-94, the County Physician, and an accomplished surgeon at O'Connor Sanitarium until his death in February, 1906.

And Dr. Abraham McMahon, a Union Army surgeon, came to San José in 1875 and made friends quickly. He was elected County Coroner in 1876, and served as County Physician in 1878-79. His son, John, also became a doctor and the two were partners for many years.

Few men could match the medical background of Missourian Dr. John S. Potts, who studied in New York City's Bellevue Hospital, Vienna, Berlin, Paris, Dublin, London and Edinburgh. His wife's delicate health sent him searching the world over for a salubrious climate. Each visit convinced him San José's was the answer. Launching his practice in 1875, Dr. Potts excelled in many fields. He was one of the founders of the San José Board of Trade, a forerunner of the Chamber of Commerce. He convinced city fathers they should pro-

The Vendome Hotel shortly after it opened in 1889. It was built chiefly through the efforts of Dr. John S. Potts, who believed San Jose needed a new and fashionable hotel to attract tourists to the community. Guests were amazed at such innovations as running hot water and electric lights.

(Courtesy of San Jose Mercury-News)

ject to the world in stentorian fashion the delights of life in the Garden City. To attract visitors, he led in organizing a corporation to build the sumptuous Vendome Hotel at First and Hobson Streets. It opened in grand style in 1889 with big bay windows and such innovations as electric lights and hot running water.

The Seiferts added another chapter in the valley's father-son medical tradition. William Seifert was a German who was graduated from the University of Magdeburg. He practiced in Santa Clara from 1854 until his death in 1884. His son, George W., was one of the first physicians born in Santa Clara County. A graduate of Santa Clara College in 1879, George W.

Seifert studied in the East until 1884 when he returned to become the college's physician, a position he held eight years. He increased his education in Vienna, and in 1895 he joined the O'Connor Sanitarium staff.

A bachelor all his life, Dr. Seifert willed his estate valued at $250,000 to Santa Clara College, which triggered one of California's longest and most bitterly fought litigations. The will was contested by collateral kin in Germany and it took 14 years before the college won out. The adjudication was very costly. The remaining funds were used to erect the Seifert Gymnasium, as well as Seifert Gate at the Franklin and Alviso Street entrance to the campus. The

Dr. George W. Seifert, whose father, William, also practiced medicine in Santa Clara. George Seifert was one of the first Santa Clara College graduates to practice in the Valley. The Seifert Gymnasium and Seifert Gate honor his name on the campus.

Dr. Elizabeth Gallimore, one of the first Santa Clara Valley natives to practice medicine in San Jose. Highly respected by her colleagues, she was secretary of the Santa Clara County Medical Society for many years.

gymnasium opened in 1924 and accommodated hundreds of major athletic events in ensuing years.

There were few women doctors in San José before 1879. Then, Dr. Euthanasia S. Meade, with weighty credentials, came upon the scene and she soon won over her doubting colleagues with her medical talent and acumen. She had become interested in the profession during the Civil War when she nursed Union Army wounded at St. Joseph's Hospital in Philadelphia. Educated at the University of Pennsylvania and in Europe, Dr. Meade arrived in San José as the third bona fide woman physician in California. She found San José's climate beneficial for her chronic bronchial asthma. Before her death in 1895, she

played a major role in organizing the state's women physicians. The organization was called the Woman's Medical Club of the Pacific. Dr. Meade was elected president and delivered the inaugural address at its initial convention. Her junior partner for three years was Dr. Elizabeth Gallimore. She was a native of Santa Clara Valley and a graduate of the University of the Pacific. Dr. Gallimore was recording secretary for the County Medical Society for many years.

The medical society was a smooth-functioning organization through the Eighties, except for an occasional complaint from outlying physicians about the difficulty of travel to the meetings.

"Doctors are the best-natured people in

the world—except when they get to fighting each other," Oliver Wendall Holmes once observed while lecturing at Harvard. This was exemplified in 1898 when a dispute over contrasting schools of medicine caused a rift in the County Medical Society. The organization, then numbering 50 doctors, passed a resolution attacking as unethical the practice of consulting with "irregular practitioners." This referred to homopaths, exponents of a doctrine first espoused by a German, Dr. Samuel Hahnemann, a half century before. Homeopathy is the science of curing diseases with very minute doses of medicine which in a healthy person would produce a condition like that of the disease treated. It was based on the ancient scheme of "a hair of the dog that bit you." On the opposite side, and in the vast majority, were the allopaths. They sought to cure disease by producing in a person's system a condition different from or incompatible with that of the disease. Holmes sardonically derided homeopathy as "a mingled mass of perverse ingenuity, of tinsel erudition, of imbecile credulity and of artful misrepresentation."

Several doctors, led by Frederick H. Bangs and William Simpson, defended the practice of homeopathy. This academic dispute, plus a clash of personalities in the society's upper echelon, led to the schism and it took several years before comity among the medical clan was re-established.

Valley physicians occasionally were invited to special autopsies. In 1882, a Juan Wasielewsky of San José stabbed his Mexican wife to death because she sought to divorce him while he was serving a prison sentence for cattle stealing. Wasielewsky evaded capture until 1884 when he was apprehended, tried and hanged.

Dr. J. L. Berry, County Medical Society president, sent invitations to doctors to observe the autopsy on Wasielewsky's body at the South First Street morgue at 2 p.m., October 24. It was performed by a San Francisco pathologist. Doctors especially wanted to test the theory that a criminal's brain was of abnormal size. Wasielewsky's, it turned out, was normal.

The medical society meetings were regularly reported by the *San José Mercury*, often on page one. The widely known Dr. James R. Curnow read a paper on April 2, 1889, entitled *"The Origin of Diseases."*

"Diseases come from four causes," Dr. Curnow said. "The first are those absorbed through the pore of the cuticle; second, those breathed from the atmosphere; third,

Dr. William Simpson was a homeopathic physician who was named San Jose's first official health officer in 1889. He also was Santa Clara County physician during the influenza epidemic of 1918.

taken in with food and drink, and fourth, thermal or climatic."

Dr. Simpson, the Canadian-born homeopathic physician and educator, came to San José in 1881. He was one of the area's first eye, ear, nose and throat specialists. In 1889, he was named San José's first health officer. He was the first to keep and preserve vital statistics for the community. Dr. Simpson was the city's oldest practitioner when he died in 1928.

The *San José Mercury* in January, 1890, quoted Dr. Simpson's semi-annual health report. He said that only 150 persons had died in the second six months of 1889. This was a rate of 12 per 1,000, lower than any other city in the country outside of California. Twenty-five per cent of the deaths were caused by consumption.

The advent of O'Connor Sanitarium created quite a ripple in the valley's medical ranks. Drs. Alexander L. Prevost and Walter Thorne applied for the position of chief physician. Sister Severina believed the paucity of patients in those first few months, plus the fact many were non-ailing oldsters, made hiring of a physician unnecessary. The O'Connors concurred, writing from Germany:

"We agree heartily in your review regarding the employment of a resident physician, for he would be about as much service as a fifth wheel to a coach."

The touring O'Connors once discussed the merits of Dr. Pedro Merlin Lusson, a slightly built Cuban of French-German descent whose family owned a coffee plantation. He had come to Santa Clara Valley as a sick man in 1873, but the salubrious clime soon had him on his feet. The O'Connors wrote the sisters that Dr. Lusson's employment as chief of staff was strictly up to them, but he appeared "too delicate" to

J. Underwood Hall Jr., the first chief of staff at O'Connor Sanitarium. He practiced for 57 years, most of them in San Jose.

handle the sanitarium's growing patient load.

By far the most influential physician in O'Connor Sanitarium's budding years was Dr. J. Underwood Hall Jr. He, too, was a member of a father-son medical tandem. J. Underwood Sr., born in Kentucky in 1822, had been a rugged adventurer. At age 17, he was 6 ft. 4½ in and weighed 175 pounds. He farmed until he was 22 when a brother, P. J. Hall, persuaded him to enter medicine. He began his studies in Louisville, Kentucky, medical center of the Midwest in that era. But in 1852, he followed the call of gold to California, making the 35-day trip by sea. For six years, he practiced medicine and mined for gold. He related in the family archives of his first call as a doctor, receiving an ounce of gold for removing sutures from a miner's wound.

In Kanaka Camp, he sacked one thousand dollars in gold dust in three months. At Orleans Flat, he formed an express company to haul gold and in six months netted fifty thousand dollars.

The senior Hall returned to the East in 1858, earning his medical degree from Jefferson Medical College in Philadelphia. He joined the Union Army in 1860 and was appointed Post Surgeon at Lexington (Kentucky) Military Hospital. He was captured in 1863 by Confederate General John Morgan in a daring raid and confined at Knoxville, Tennessee, but he was returned to the Union side later in an exchange of prisoners. He was in Kentucky when he received word from California of a personal catastrophe. A dam had collapsed on the Eureka Ditch, a water project in which he had invested heavily. The disaster wiped out his fortune except for two thousand dollars. Late in 1863, he decided to try his luck in the Comstock Lode. He combined mining with medicine at Gold Hill, Nevada's second largest settlement located two miles from boisterous Virginia City. He

returned east to marry a Kentucky girl in 1865 and brought her back to Gold Hill.

Hall built a big home and in a few years it was filled with nine children. His lanky physique and stovepipe hat made him a familiar sight in the teeming mining communities. In 1866, he was named Surgeon General for Nevada, a position he held for 12 years. In his memoirs, he noted making $140,000 in the Comstock over 20 years. But he was able to bring only a small part of that amount to the Santa Clara Valley because of the high cost of living in the Nevada mining country, especially for a family of 11.

The senior Hall's second son was born February 9, 1868, in Gold Hill. J. Underwood Hall Jr. started his medical studies at the University of California School of Pharmacy when he was but 17. The next year he went to the New Almaden quicksilver mines where he was a druggist, clerk and aide to the camp surgeon, Dr. S. E. Winn. After study at Cooper Medical College in San Francisco and Jefferson Medical College of Philadelphia, the same school at-

Dr. J. Underwood Hall, Jr. (right) performs operation in O'Connor Sanitarium about 1918. At left is the sanitarium administrator, Sister Zoe. Dr. Hall was the institution's first staff physician.

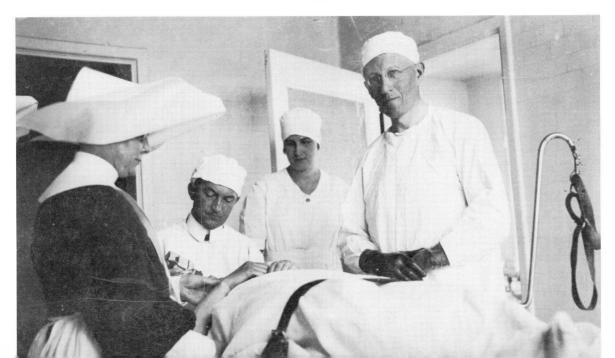

tended by his father, young Hall returned to New Almaden in the summer of 1889. When he was offered the camp surgeon's position succeeding the aging Dr. Winn, some miners were highly upset. They believed a lad of 21 too young for the job. But Hall's background, plus the reputation of his father who once had held the post, won over most of the mining camp.

The young physician attempted to look older by growing a mustache and beard. His salary was $250 a month, with house and horse provided. In 1894, Dr. Hall resigned and went to Chicago to study under one of the nation's foremost surgeons, Dr. Nicholas Senn. He then went to New York's Roosevelt Hospital to learn from the celebrated Dr. Charles McBurney. This was a big year for Dr. Hall. Upon his return to San José, he opened a downtown office and on December 27 married Grace Spencer. The marriage united him with the family of the famed forty-niner physician, A. J. Spencer.

In a few weeks, Dr. Hall became an integral part of the O'Connor Sanitarium story. By arrangement with the sisters, he would drive out in his buggy each day to care for patients. He was a potent force in the sanitarium's operations for 25 years, his last term as president of the medical staff coming in 1919. A San José magazine, *The Sketch*, listed the six members of the O'Connor staff on December 16, 1899; Dr. J. Underwood Hall, president; and Dr. John D. Grissim, Dr. George W. Fowler, Dr. Chauncey R. Burr, Dr. George W. Seifert, and Dr. Elizabeth Gallimore, physicians.

Dr. Hall often confided to friends that, although he was not a Catholic, he enjoyed his long association with the sanitarium because of his admiration and respect for the Daughters of Charity.

At 6 feet and 170 pounds, Dr. Hall was smaller than his father. Slender and graceful, he was easily recognizable by his rimless spectacles and thinning blond hair fading into gray. He was regarded as one of the area's three outstanding surgeons for many years. Automobiles were a favorite hobby. He was constantly changing cars, driving some 20 different Franklins over the years.

Dr. Hall was a fearless individual, having no regard for physical danger. Once about 1915, he was called to the scene of a murder where a handyman had gone berserk in a home off The Alameda. Dr. Hall arrived moments after the sheriff and his deputy and it was feared the murderer was still on the grounds. The law being in no hurry to invade the darkness, Dr. Hall took a lantern and with his chauffeur scoured the area without results.

Dr. Hall retired briefly to Santa Barbara after World War I, then opened a practice in San Francisco where he continued to treat many of his longtime San José patients. His death came after 57 years of practice.

A son, Santa Clara County Superior Court Judge Marshall Hall, disclosed that Dr. Hall diagnosed his own illness—a rare type of bone cancer.

"How long do you have?" the son asked one day when informed of Dr. Hall's diagnosis.

"Six months, maybe longer."

"What are you going to do?"

"Continue working. It's not a contagious disease. I can still help others."

He died on October 25, 1946, at the age of 78.

Over the first century of valley medicine, Dr. George Washington Fowler's

Dr. George Washington Fowler, whose career as a practicing physician extended 61½ years, the longest of any doctor in Santa Clara Valley history. He retired from his Santa Clara practice in 1953 and died at the age of 95 in 1962.

name held a high place. When he retired at the age of 85 in 1952, he had put in 61½ years of practice. He was born on Fowler Road on the valley's east side. His father, Andrew Jackson Fowler, came across the plains to California in 1852 and was remembered well into the 20th century for the tall stands of eucalyptus trees he planted along Alum Rock Avenue. (The trees, until their removal in the 1950's, were among the oldest in California; the state's first eucalyptus still stands on Schallenberger Road, having been planted by Captain Joseph Aram in 1858.)

A graduate of Santa Clara College in 1888, he continued his schooling at the University of Pennsylvania Medical School.

On his death, he made Philadelphia newspaper headlines as the venerable school's oldest alumnus.

Upon his graduation, the university surprised Fowler by offering him a position as full professor of gynecology.

"I'll have to think it over," replied Fowler, an honor student and class valedictorian.

"Think it over!" said startled university officials, who were making an unprecedented overture. "You can't say no."

"I certainly appreciate the offer," Fowler responded. "But you see I grew up in California where one doesn't freeze all winter and perspire all summer. I think that's where I want to practice medicine."

Dr. Fowler began his career on June 13, 1892, in partnership with Dr. George W. Seifert. He made regular visits to O'Connor Sanitarium where he offered his services to the sisters. Holder of a degree in pharmacy, he often put up prescriptions for Sister Fidelis until she was qualified to assume the task herself. He carried keys for every pharmacy in the area so that he could enter at any time to make up emergency prescriptions.

Dr. Fowler was County Hospital administrator-supervisor in 1903-07 and his staff consisted of but a single practical nurse. He instituted the hospital's first system of records.

The Santa Clara doctor was a good surgeon but was in actual practice the equivalent of the present day internist. Often, when he was unable to obtain a surgical nurse, he would call across the street to a neighbor, Santa Clara County Supervisor John Roll. The supervisor had a strong stomach and good hands and was an excellent surgical assistant.

Dr. Fowler's competence was widely

recognized in the community. On one occasion, a young girl was believed dead from pneumonia. A neighbor refused to accept the pronouncement until it had been verified by Dr. Fowler. He hurried to the girl's bedside and during the examination detected a faint heart beat, a common characteristic of severe pneumonia cases. He saved her life and she grew up to bear 13 children.

"I often wonder if that woman, with all those youngsters running around, doesn't sometimes wish I hadn't let her die in peace," Dr. Fowler would chuckle to friends.

With a quiver of his heavy eyebrows that shaded glistening brown eyes, Dr. Fowler insisted patients follow his instructions to the letter. One time, he gave an ailing man some medicine and told him to rest. The next day, Dr. Fowler was driving past the man's home and noticed him working in his yard. Bolting out of his car, the physician upbraided the man at length. "Now, you get to bed and stay there," Dr. Fowler exclaimed. Three weeks later a little girl knocked at the door of the Fowler residence. When the doctor answered he found her near tears.

"What is it, young lady?" he asked.

Identifying herself, she said:

"Dr. Fowler, my father wants to know if it would be all right to get out of bed now."

Dr. Fowler served Santa Clara as a high school trustee for many years. He proposed school-sponsored dances where students could be properly chaperoned rather than frequent the often rowdy dance halls in the area.

Dr. Fowler always took pride in never pressing a patient for payment of a bill. "Give people half a chance and they'll get you the money if they have it," he would say.

Dr. Fowler was so broken up over his wife's death that he actually put away his medical kit. But his old patients talked him into returning to practice. He practiced several more years before quitting for good on Washington's Birthday, 1953. He lived in easy retirement almost a decade before his death in October, 1962, at the age of 95.

A classmate of Dr. Fowler's at Pennsylvania was Frederick C. Gerlach, who became one of the Santa Clara Valley's most accomplished and colorful physicians.

Dr. Gerlach, born in Los Gatos in 1873, lived all his life in the valley except for occasional trips abroad. His father was the head tailor at Spring's Clothing Store in San José. Gerlach was graduated from Santa Clara College with a master of science degree in 1891. At Pennsylvania Medical School he was an outstanding athlete. He competed on the boxing team and went with the crew to England for several big races.

Dr. Frederick G. Gerlach, a prominent San Jose physician and surgeon for almost a half century. He was a three-time president of the O'Connor Sanitarium medical staff.

Dr. Frederick C. Gerlach poses with a Santa Clara College brother who aided him in treatment of patients at the institution. The mission is in the background. Dr. Gerlach, whose hobby was automobiles, was the college physician until shortly before his death when he was succeeded by Dr. Edward Amaral.

He was so youthful in appearance when he opened practice in San José that he found it necessary, as did Dr. Hall, to grow a beard and mustache. In the Nineties, he often made his rounds on a bicycle.

Dr. Gerlach was the physician for Santa Clara College during most of the years in which he practiced. He was an avid automobile enthusiast and his patients never knew from week to week whether he'd be driving a Stanley Steamer, Stutz Bearcat or some other new make. Even in his later years he was known for his athletic prowess, be it fishing, hunting, boxing, fencing or billiards.

Upon his marriage to Regina Krieg in May, 1928, Dr. Gerlach took a six-month, round-the-world trip. He made a study of diseases in the Orient and attended medical clinics in Europe. He visited Vienna several times to keep abreast of surgical techniques.

Dr. Gerlach's reputation was evidenced in one incident when he was approached by well-to-do San José parents concerned over their daughter. He examined her and found she was afflicted with a stomach abnormality. The parents leaned strongly toward surgery, but Dr. Gerlach advised against it. Such surgery still was in the experimental stage although he felt he could do it if an emergency presented itself.

The parents, unhappy with Dr. Gerlach's recommendation, took the girl to the Mayo Clinic for intensive tests. The clinic reported the girl did have a hiatus hernia, but surgery was not recommended unless absolutely necessary.

The San José family still was dissatisfied and decided to go to Vienna to consult the world's finest surgeons. One of Vienna's most noted physicians greeted the parents in his office.

"And where are you from?" he asked them.

"We are from the United States," they answered.

"Where in the United States?"

"California."

"California! Do you know Dr. Frederick Gerlach?"

"Yes, we know him."

"Did you take your girl's problem to Dr. Gerlach?"

"Yes, we did."

"What did he say?"

"He said not to operate."

"If Dr. Gerlach said no operation, we say no operation."

Dr. Gerlach, O'Connor staff president three times (1915, 1920, 1921), often seemed gruff and harsh to some acquaintances. But his closest friends knew him as a gentle, soft-hearted man who was among the most popular and skilled physicians and surgeons of his day. He died in 1945 at the age of 72.

Other prominent physicians on the O'Connor staff by 1912 were David A. Beattie, John Irving Beattie, James C. Blair, T. L. Blanchard, Jonas Clark, Ada Scott Conner, Alfred W. Conner, Eugene A. Filipello, Robert L. Hogg, Mark F. Hopkins, J. J. Kocher, Arthur T. McGinty, Antrim Edgar Osborne, Charles M. Richards, William S. Van Dalsem, Samuel B. Van Dalsem and Doxey R. Wilson.

Dr. David A. Beattie was an eminent surgeon in Santa Clara Valley for 40 years until his death in 1935. He was graduated from the Trinity Medical School of the University of Toronto, Canada. He then went to Canton, China, to begin his practice. He founded a dispensary in 1893 at Yung Kong, which for a long time was the largest medical center in southern China.

The illness of Dr. Beattie's wife compelled them to come to California. He won respect throughout the San José region for his medical skill and he was active in political circles. Dr. Beattie's son, William Douglas, became a celebrated opera singer. He launched his career in San José, later making his debut in 1934 at Genoa, Italy. He sang on the concert stage with the New York Metropolitan and the San Francisco Opera Companies. Douglas retired to a fruit ranch shortly before World War II in Porterville, where he died.

Dr. John Irving Beattie was the nephew of David A. Beattie. Also a Canadian by birth, he came to Santa Clara in 1907 after graduation from Cooper Medical College in San Francisco and study at a London hospital. At Cooper, he was a classmate of Dr. Walter C. Alvarez, the physician-author. John Irving Beattie, like his uncle, was a kind, gentle family doctor of the old school. He headed the O'Connor medical staff in 1923. He died at 59 in 1943.

Dr. Jonas Clark, a native of Waltham, Mass., was a versatile person who stood out in many medical fields. A graduate of Massachusetts Institute of Technology, he attended medical school at Harvard where

Dr. Robert L. Hogg, pioneer Santa Clara Valley physician who was also a prominent civic leader in the Saratoga-Los Gatos area.

he did class dissections under the watchful eye of Oliver Wendell Holmes.

Dr. Clark appeared set for life as surgeon for the Massachusetts Charitable Eye and Ear Infirmary in Boston until poor health brought him westward. He practiced in Woodland and San Francisco and finally, in 1890, he moved to Gilroy. He was superintendent of Santa Clara County Hospital in 1910-13 and for 10 years was district surgeon for the Southern Pacific Railroad. In his later years, he turned over the reins of his office to his son, John A. Clark. A graduate of Santa Clara College and the University of California Medical School, Dr. John A. Clark practiced 50 years

in southern Santa Clara County. He died in 1958.

Dr. John A. Clark's daughter continued the family's medical tradition. Dr. Mary Clark is now chief of the Bureau of Preventive Medicine, Santa Clara County Health Department.

Dr. Ada Scott Conner (later Ada Scott Conner Morton Lewis Wells) was an active valley physician for 25 years and she also had a hectic marital record. She was said to have charged up to five thousand dollars for an appendectomy in the early days when the mortality rate for such surgeries was high. Her first husband, Dr. Alfred W. Conner, practiced more than fifty years in the valley. He died in 1965. She became Dr. Ada Scott Connor Morton Lewis when she married heavyweight wrestler Ed (Strangler) Lewis, for whom she built a private swimming pool and other features in their east Santa Clara Valley home during the height of his career. She practiced three years in San Francisco (1927-30) and then retired to a lemon grove ranch at Fallbrook, California, where she died in January, 1939.

Dr. Filipello came to the valley in 1896 from his birthplace near Turino, Italy, through the efforts of a brother working on the Doyle Ranch in Cupertino.

Short and stocky and sporting a mustache (and occasionally a goatee), Dr. Filipello was the leading physician for Italian-speaking San José residents for many years. When thieves kept making off with his bicycles, he switched to a horse and buggy and finally to a Hudson coupé to call on his patients.

Dr. Filipello was instrumental in bringing Dr. E. A. Turco to San José in 1921. Dr. Turco had been a major in the Italian Army medical staff in World War I. Super-

Dr. Frank W. Knowles, early-day Los Gatos physician and community leader. He was a Santa Clara County supervisor at the turn of the century. His wife was the daughter of John Bean, founder of the forerunner of the Food Machinery Corporation.

Dr. James W. Thayer, who came to Gilroy in the 1880s and took an active role in the city's development. He was a leading member of the City Council for many years.

intendent Doxey R. Wilson of the County Hospital found employment for Dr. Turco, who could not speak a word of English, and Dr. John Irving Beattie helped the newcomer in his studies to acquire California medical credentials. Dr. Turco is still practicing. Dr. Filipello died at 83 in July, 1954.

Kentucky-born Dr. Robert L. Hogg was for many years the only physician in Saratoga. He practiced for 30 years and then retired to devote time to other interests in

1927. He developed the Hogg Building business center, was a director of the Blossom Festival, helped organize the Saratoga State Bank and the Saratoga Inn and was an original trustee of Los Gatos Union High School District. He died in November, 1956, at the age of 83.

Other pioneer healers who blended their practices with civic leadership were Drs. Frank W. Knowles and Robert P. Gober of Los Gatos, Charles N. Cooper and Walter I. Merrill of Campbell, Louis Mendelsohn of Saratoga, Reuben L. Newbold, Louis V. Saph and Robert T. Higgins of Morgan Hill, Frank E. Buck of Mayfield (Palo Alto), Caleb V. Jones of Mountain View, and Heverland R. Chesbro, Hugh Schmitt and James W. Thayer of Gilroy.

Dr. Knowles initiated his practice in 1883 after graduation from Rush Medical College in Chicago. He was a County Supervisor in 1900. At his death in 1935, he was 78 years old. Dr. Gober came to Los Gatos in 1884, fresh out of Bellevue Medical School in New York City. In 1886, he married Annette Bean, daughter of a Michigan inventor, John Bean, who was founder of a pump manufacturing company in San José. The Bean firm was the forerunner of the giant Food Machinery Corporation. At the time of his retirement in 1935 after 51 years of practice, Dr. Gober's partner was Dr. Horace G. Jones (O'Connor staff president in 1936). Dr. Gober died at 84 in March, 1943.

Dr. Walter I. Merrill, born in Maine in 1886, arrived in Campbell in 1911. His grandfather, Edmund T. Merrill, had been the shipbuilder who fastened the metal plates to the Monitor for its historic sea battle with the Merrimac in the Civil War. Dr. Merrill was O'Connor Sanitarium chief of staff in 1943. He was instrumental in forming Sanitation District Four before he retired from medicine and moved to Southern California.

Leaving Boston in favor of rural Saratoga, Harvard-educated Dr. Louis Mendelsohn arrived in 1922. He treated patients for 27 years before his retirement in 1949. He was active in Saratoga civic life and was an accomplished violinist. Shortly before his death at 71 in November, 1950, part of the Los Gatos-Saratoga Road was

Dr. Louis Mendelsohn, a graduate of Harvard who practiced for 27 years in Saratoga. He was revered as a community leader and was an accomplished violinist as well.

re-named Mendelsohn Lane in the physician's honor.

Dr. Saph, a San José native, practiced in his hometown from 1897 to 1922. He then became a walnut farmer near Morgan Hill. Soon afterward, however, he returned to his medical practice. He later became Justice of the Peace in Burnett Township and police judge in Morgan Hill. He retired in 1939 and died at 70 in 1945.

Two sons of Dr. Heverland R. Chesbro, a homeopathic physician who came to Gilroy in 1883, followed him into medicine. They are Drs. Elmer J. and Wayne Chesbro. Elmer is a veteran conservationist for whom Chesbro Dam is named. Death

Dr. Arthur T. McGinty was a prominent family physician in San Jose for 43 years. He was O'Connor Sanitarium chief of staff in 1922.

Dr. Antrim E. Osborne, who pioneered in medical care of feeble-minded children. He also was a California state senator.

claimed the elder Dr. Chesbro at 91 in 1947.

Dr. J. J. Kocher practiced in San José only from 1905 to 1911 when he moved to Palm Springs. He helped develop the desert city as a poular resort. His parents, Rudolph and Anna Kocher, had come to the valley to establish a pioneer jewelry firm in 1868 and it remained in the family for more than 90 years.

Dr. Arthur T. McGinty, a native of Pennsylvania, was a physician and surgeon in San José for 43 years. He maintained offices for several years in the Sainte Claire Building, and later at 279 South Third Street. He was O'Connor chief of staff in 1922. Dr. McGinty's daughter, Marcella, was married to District Attorney N. J. Menard. Another daughter, Aileen, became

the wife of Dr. Frank J. Volpe, a pediatrician now practicing in San José. Dr. McGinty died in 1949.

Dr. Antrim Edgar Osborne, born in Pennsylvania in 1856, carried both M.D. and Ph. D. degrees and put them to good use.

On December 1, 1886, he became superintendent of the California Home for the Care and Training of Feeble-Minded Children on the west edge of Santa Clara. He was the head of the only institution of its kind west of Nebraska. He later operated a sanitarium between Santa Clara and Campbell and he helped organize the Santa Clara County Historical Society.

Dr. Osborne was elected to the California State Senate in the Twenties. The *Sacramento Union* on April 21, 1921, termed

The Richards Club, a male chorus organized by Dr. Charles M. Richards. Formed in 1914, it was active more than 40 years and its members included several physicians.

Dr. Osborne "the most popular man in the senate." Dr. Osborne also served as superintendent of the Sonoma State Hospital and the Napa State Hospital.

Dr. Charles M. Richards, Dr. N. H. Bullock and Dr. James B. Bullitt were pioneer San José radiologists.

Dr. Richards, a native of Watsonville, established the radiology department at San José Hospital. At the time of his retirement, he was associated with Dr. John W. H. von Saltza, the highly respected radiologist whose daughter, Chris, was a world-renowned swimming champion. She won four gold medals at the 1960 Olympic Games in Rome. A gifted musician, Dr. Richards founded the San José Elks Orchestra, which developed into the San José Symphony. In 1914, he founded the Richards Club, a male chorus active in San José

Dr. Charles M. Richards, who founded the radiology department at San Jose Hospital. He also formed the San Jose Elks Orchestra, forerunner of the San Jose Symphony.

more than 40 years. Dr. Richards was 75 at his death in 1957.

Dr. Bullock practiced in San José for twenty years during which time he was president of the County Health Center and a medical examiner for city schools and San José State College. He died in 1929.

Dr. Bullitt moved to San José in the earthquake year, 1906. He was a Kentuckian who had studied at the University of Louisville, Bonn University and the University of Heidelberg. In 1904, he was president of the American Roentgen Ray Society. He lived on Penitencia Creek Road at Noble Avenue. He developed the Bullitt mastoid apparatus, which was used for many years in x-raying the mastoid region. He was 83 at his death in 1945.

Dr. William S. Van Dalsem, a resident of San José from 1888, was a prominent general practitioner until his death in San Francisco in 1941. He served for 16 years as a San José Board of Education member. His daughter, Frances, became the wife of San José City Manager A. P. Hamann. His brother, Dr. Samuel B. Van Dalsem, began his practice in Palo Alto, then moved to San José where he practiced for 28 years. He assisted in organizing the San José Medical Dental Building and later came out of retirement during World War II to establish and operate the Joshua Hendy Iron Works Medical Service in Sunnyvale. He died at 74 in 1949. His son, Volney, is a general surgeon with the San José Medical Clinic.

Dr. Doxey R. Wilson, a 1908 graduate of Cooper Medical College, served his internship at Santa Clara County Hospital. It was a place he called home for a long time. He was superintendent there for 27 years (1913-1940). He wore many hats at the hospital, including those of administra-

Dr. Doxey R. Wilson, who served as Santa Clara County Hospital superintendent for 27 year, wore a mustache in the early twenties.

tor, surgeon, purchasing agent and bookkeeper. He then went into private practice with his son, Dr. John C. Wilson. The elder Dr. Wilson died after a household fall at 72 in 1956.

Opening practice in San José in 1916 was Dr. J. Samuel Staub, who came from a family of medical men in Berlin where he was born on May 23, 1885. He was a veteran staff member at O'Connor Hospital after serving as resident physician at the Southern Pacific Hospital in San Francisco. Dr. Staub is regarded as an authority in railroad accident cases and often testifies in court. He is a specialist in industrial surgery.

Three physicians—E. Paul Cook, Fred S. Ryan and Henry E. Dahleen—served both as O'Connor chiefs of staff and County Hospital superintendents.

Dr. E. Paul Cook opened practice as the valley's first pediatrician in 1920. A native Minnesotan, he had been educated at the University of California. Other pediatricians such as Dr. Lucas Empey and Dr. Karl F. Pelkan soon followed, but most doctors in the Twenties were general practitioners.

Dr. Cook maintained his private practice until 1957 when he assumed administration of the public assistance medical care program in San José for the county and the state. He was interim director of the County Hospital in 1961. He retired after 44 years of practice in 1964. President of the O'Connor staff in 1930, Dr. Cook was instrumental in developing the valley's first

Dr. Fred S. Ryan practiced in Santa Clara Valley for 29 years until his death in 1940. He was O'Connor Sanitarium chief of staff in 1924 and Santa Clara County Hospital superintendent in 1940.

Dr. E. Paul Cook, the Santa Clara Valley's first pediatrician. He developed the area's first pediatrics department at O'Connor Sanitarium in 1928.

pediatrics department in a private hospital in 1928 at O'Connor's.

The physician's son, Dr. Sheldon Cook, is a pediatrician at Lafayette in Alameda County. The elder Dr. Cook's daughter, Carolyn, is married to Laurence J. Kennedy of Redding, a University of California Regent.

Dr. Ryan, O'Connor chief of staff in 1924 and County Hospital superintendent for four months until he died of a coronary thrombosis in 1940, began his practice in the valley in 1911 after study at the University of California and Northwestern University. The highly revered Dr. Ryan was first stricken in 1934 while hiking in the Trinity Alps of Northern California.

But thanks to the help of his lifelong friend, Dr. R. Stanley Kneeshaw, Dr. Ryan was returned home safely and he recovered to resume his practice. He was only 58 at the time of his death. A daughter, Margaret, became the wife of internist Dr. Paul V. Morton of the San José Medical Clinic.

Dr. Dahleen, a native of Granite Falls, Minnesota, was in both private and public medical service in San José for more than thirty years. Previously, he was a staff member of the Mayo Clinic in 1917-20. A pioneer San José urologist, he was O'Connor staff president in 1925 and County Hospital superintendent in 1940-52. He was 74 at his death in 1956. His son, Henry C., a general surgeon, worked with Dr. Paul V. Morton in founding the Medical Clinic in 1955.

Dr. Milton J. Chatton succeeded Dr. Dahleen as Director of Santa Clara County Medical Institutions and he revitalized all the programs under his control. A native of Fresno, he received his M.D. from the University of California in 1943. After wartime military service, he became medical director of the University of California Hospital Clinics in San Francisco. Assuming the Santa Clara County post in 1952, he developed the highly successful medical education program at County Hospital, established modern new administrative procedures, and gave impetus to the physicians' voluteer service system. He led the 1955 and 1956 bond issue campaigns and helped design the new seven-story, seven million dollar wing that opened in 1960 as well as the total master plan. Dr. Chatton resigned in 1958 to enter private practice. He currently is consultant in San José for the State Department of Rehabilitation and is an author and medical editor for the Lange Medical Publications of Los

Altos, the world's largest medical publishing house.

Dr. R. Morton Manson was instrumental in development of the County Hospital's outstanding intern and residency programs. He directed the hospital's tuberculosis division from 1951 to 1959, when he was named Director of Clinical Services. The hospital's medical education program, which began in 1919, in 1965 listed 32 interns and 62 resident physicians. Among non-university hospitals, it boasts one of the major medical education programs in the nation.

The County Hospital, now under the direction of Dr. Norman B. Nelson, has come a long way since Dr. G. B. Crane in 1855 contracted to see up to seven patients a day. Admissions now run more than 13,000 a year and patients attended by all departments total 170,000 a year. There are 29 full and half-time physicians on the staff today. Five hundred staff physicians volunteer 18,000 hours a year. A seven million dollar expansion program, which will greatly increase out-patient, emergency, radiology and laboratory facilities, presently is being planned.

Dr. Louis M. Rose owned the first electrocardiograph in Santa Clara Valley in 1935. A native of Poland, Dr. Rose maintained an office on Main Street in Santa Clara for many years. Head of the O'Connor medical staff in 1931, he practiced for 30 years. He was an expert wood carver and examples of his wood artistry were featured frequently at California Medical Association conventions. He was 67 when he died in October, 1949.

Dr. John J. Miller's name was well known in the valley for his dedication to medicine and community service. His career began in 1880 when he was graduated from the

University of Michigan. Before coming to San José, he practiced in Kansas City and Clifton, Arizona, where he was physician for the Arizona Copper Company. Arriving in the Santa Clara Valley in 1889, he practiced until his retirement in 1919.

He served two terms as County Health Officer and, about 1900, he traveled to India to report on the effect of tuberculin tests in diagnosis of tuberculosis. As a member of the Board of Freeholders, he helped draft the San José City Charter when the city manager form of municipal government was adopted. He was 87 at his death in 1946. His son, Dr. John J. Miller, Jr., was a clinical professor at the Stanford University School of Medicine at his death in 1953.

Dr. John Hunt Shephard recorded a third of a century of medical service before his retirement at 73 in 1952. Head of the staff at O'Connor in 1926, he had brought an impressive background to San José from his native Iowa. He was a graduate of Rush Medical College in Chicago and was a staff member of the Mayo Clinic. Dr. Shephard, while on the San José Hospital staff, was instrumental in formation of a hospitalization insurance program which later became the Blue Cross. He was a strong booster of the O'Connor fund drive in the Forties. Dr. Shephard died at 78 in September, 1957.

Few figures were more influential in the latter-day development of O'Connor's than Dr. Earl O. G. Schmitt.

A two-time president of the O'Connor staff (1932, 1948), the Minnesota-born physician was the son of a prominent banker. Receiving his medical degree from the University of Minnesota, Dr. Schmitt interned at Providence Hospital in Detroit. He was a fellow at the Mayo Clinic before coming to San José in 1928 to join Drs. Dahleen and Shephard. Dr. Schmitt was one of the area's first internists, following in the footsteps of Drs. George A. Gray and C. Kelly Canelo.

Dr. John Hunt Shephard came to San Jose from the famed Mayo Clinic. He played a part in formation of the hospitalization insurance program which later became the Blus Cross.

Dr. Earl O. G. Schmitt, one of Santa Clara Valley's first internists. He was one of the key campaigners for construction of the new O'Connor Hospital.

Dr. Schmitt was active in community service organizations and was a key leader in the O'Connor fund drive in the late Forties. He was in the forefront in planning and executing the concept of the new hospital. He died at 63 in 1962 of a heart ailment in his home on The Alameda.

A tragic death cut short the career of Dr. Adolph J. Baiocchi at the age of 53 on February 16, 1945.

Dr. Baiocchi was stricken the previous December 23 with typhoid fever after he returned from a duck hunting trip near Warm Springs in Alameda County. He was believed to have contracted the disease by accidentally ingesting vegetables that had been washed in polluted water.

The general practitioner waged a seven-week battle for life and the O'Connor Sanitarium switchboard was deluged by calls asking his condition. A San José native, he attended St. Joseph's School, the University of Santa Clara and Stanford University Medical School before launching his practice. Holder of a diploma from the University of Vienna, which he visited with his wife in 1929, Dr. Baiocchi was a specialist in abdominal surgery. He was O'Connor staff president in 1927. In 1934, he opened a "semi-clinic" designed to bridge the gap between the physician's office and the hospital at 369 South Third Street. Dr. Baiocchi's half-brother, Dr. Richard T. Bigotti, was president of the O'Connor medical staff in 1951 and 1957. Dr. Bigotti, presently practicing in San José, was a member of the O'Connor executive committee for 17 years —longer than anyone in the history of the hospital.

Dr. Jacob L. Pritchard combined a medical career with many years of public service. He practiced in San José and Santa Clara from 1920 to 1942, when he entered

Dr. Jacob L. Pritchard is esteemed for his many years of medical practice. He also took part in civic activities, serving two terms as mayor of Santa Clara.

the military service and was named commanding officer of the Kohler Hospital in Sacramento for the duration of World War II. He later was mayor of Santa Clara for two terms. He was chief of the O'Connor staff in 1929. One of his eight children also entered medicine, Dr. Francis X. Pritchard of Cupertino.

Drs. Cook, Rose, Schmitt, Canelo, Kneeshaw and David B. Draper joined with Sister Superior Mary David Ingram to keep the sanitarium financially afloat during the Great Depression.

Dr. Canelo, who retired September 1, 1965, after more than 40 years of practice in San José, received his preliminary training under Dr. William Engelbach, an outstanding endocrinologist, at St. Louis

84

University. He interned under Dr. Doxey Wilson at Santa Clara County Hospital in 1923 and began his practice the next year. He lectured at the University of California Department of Endocrinology from 1930 to 1944 while practicing in San José.

In the mid-Thirties, Dr. Canelo was active in the formation of the California Physicians' Service, which provides medical care to patients on a pre-paid basis. He was a CPS trustee for five years.

Dr. Canelo was head of the O'Connor staff in 1933. In 1948, he conducted the nation's first multi-phasic chronic disease screening program in San José. The pilot survey, made under auspices of the County Medical Society, the City Health Department and the State Health Department, covered 945 employes of four San José indusrial plants. Two years later, Dr. Canelo was invited to New York City to report on the program to the American Medical Association.

Dr. Draper, an O'Connor president in 1934, was a graduate of the University of Santa Clara and St. Louis University Medical School. He was a physician and surgeon for 26 years in San José before his death in 1950.

Dr. Kneeshaw, a North Dakota-born physician who received his M.D. from Chicago's Rush Medical School, was a much-decorated Medical Corps major in recognition of his service in France during World War I. He came to San José in the early Twenties and soon established a reputation for his public service as well as his medical talents. He was O'Connor chief of staff in 1935 and president of the California Medical Association in 1949.

Dr. Helen Lee practiced more than 40 in San José. A University of Michigan graduate, she was taking her state medical

Dr. C. Kelly Canelo, a longtime San Jose physician who retired in 1965. He was prominent in the founding of the California Physicians' Service in the 1930s.

examinations in San Francisco when the 1906 earthquake struck. She specialized in gynecology and was a partner with her sister, Dr. Dorothea Lee, an eye, ear, nose and throat specialist for more than 30 years in San José. Dorothea Lee died in August, 1965. Helen Lee was active in the YWCA, serving many years as a member of the board of directors. She died in 1949.

The valley's first specialist in obstetrics and gynecology was the esteemed Dr. Alson A. Shufelt.

He first became interested in obstetrics as a five-year-old youngster in his native Nevada when his mother died in childbirth. He was a classmate of Dr. E. Paul Cook at the University of California and

Dr. David Draper, who practiced in the San Jose area for 26 years until his death in 1950. He was O'Connor Sanitarium chief of staff in 1934.

Dr. Alson A. Shufelt, Santa Clara Valley's first specialist in obstetrics. He delivered more than 9,000 babies during his 29 years of practice.

began practice in San José in 1921. He headed the obstetrics department at the County Hospital for many years.

Dr. Shufelt was said to have averaged 300 baby deliveries a year, totaling more than 9,000 during his twenty-nine years of practice. His normal twelve-hour day was expanded even more during World War II when he was the lone obstetrician in the city.

His friends believed the heavy burden he carried during the war contributed greatly to the breakdown of his health and he died of a heart ailment at 58 in June, 1950. Dr. Shufelt's associate, Dr. Francis M. Whittaker, took over his practice.

O'Connor Sanitarium Sister Superior Berenice commended Dr. Shufelt for "his

outstanding traits of charitableness, preservation of ideals in the practice of medicine, willingness to accept calls day or night and his cooperation with other members of the profession, the hospital and nurses. He will be irreplaceable in his field."

County obstetricians had founded the Shufelt Society, an informal organization of physicians in that field, while he was still alive. His death triggered a spontaneous memorial fund drive in which 152 donors contributed $1,714. It was used to purchase an anesthetic machine at San José Hospital and to establish the Shufelt Memorial Library in the obstetrics wing. He was one of the hospital founders in 1922.

Dr. Max E. Pickworth had few peers as a

86

surgeon after he opened practice in San José in 1937.

Born in Maple Creek, Saskatchewan, he was a 1930 graduate of the University of Minnesota Medical School. He then spent an additional five years in the study of surgery at Cleveland City Hospital. His 24 years of San José practice was punctuated by four years with the Army Medical Corps during World War II. He was discharged as a lieutenant colonel. While stationed at Hamilton Field, California, Dr. Pickworth performed a rare heart operation on an Arkansas army private wounded in the Battle of Leyte. A piece of shrapnel had penetrated the private's heart and the surgeon had to remove a blood clot that had formed there.

Dr. Pickworth played a significant role in the O'Connor drive for a new hospital. Only 54 years old, he was felled by a heart attack in the office of his friend, Dr. Earl O. G. Schmitt, after he had gone there to confirm fears of his condition. He died on February 14, 1961.

Dr. Frederic W. Borden's quiet and efficient years of practice as an eye, ear, nose and throat specialist in Santa Clara Valley were overshadowed only by his reputation as an inventor.

A native of Spokane, Washington, Dr. Borden early in life demonstrated his inventive genius. While living on the Canadian border, he disliked having to rise from a warm bed in the frigid morning air to build a fire. He fashionel a Rube Goldberg device out of a mousetrap to solve the problem. String attached to the alarm clock key snapped the mousetrap, to which a match was affixed. The match ignited on a board and dropped sparks onto the paper in an old wood stove. When Dr.

Dr. R. Stanley Kneeshaw, who opened practice in San Jose in the early Twenties. He was president of the California Medical Association in 1949.

Borden arose an hour later, the house was warm and comfortable.

He was a teacher for many years and learned in mechanical engineering, chemistry and physics. He finally decided to enter medicine and helped finance his way through Stanford Medical School by teaching night classes at the old San José High School.

It was while at Stanford that he developed his most successful invention—a stereoscope for three-dimensional viewing of x-rays. It enables doctors to determine how deep an object, such as a bullet or sliver, is embedded in a patient's body. It also is used routinely to observe the depth of a growth. Another invention that won its

Dr. Frederic W. Borden combined an interest in medicine with a genius for inventions. He was an eye, ear, nose and throat specialist in San Jose for 25 years.

Dr. Joseph B. Josephson, San Jose's first specialist in orthopedics. He long has been active on the O'Connor, San Jose Hospital and Santa Clara County Hospital staffs.

way into hospitals around the world was the hemorrometer which measures a patient's loss of blood during surgery.

Dr. Borden developed his inventions at his home on Stevens Creek Road. His wife, Ruth, also was mechanically inclined and ran the shop while Dr. Borden maintained his medical practice. He was a staff physician at the O'Connor Sanitarium and thought nothing of going home and making his own instruments if he felt they would improve existing facilities.

He had three adopted children and always sought to give them the same experiences he had enjoyed as a child. His father had owned a Spokane printing com-

pany and Dr. Borden made sure his children learned to read type upside down as he had done. He bought them a goat and a cow to teach them how to care for animals. When the youngsters were unable to keep up milking the cow, Dr. Borden bought a milking machine. Friends called his place "Borden's Dairy."

If anything bothered Dr. Borden, it was inefficiency. His mind was active in every field and he often would pull off the road while driving to jot notes on how to improve something he had spotted along the way.

He practiced 25 years in the valley before his death at 65 of an aortic aneurysm in

1959. Even while hospitalized, he would sit up in bed with his planning board, working on some new project.

Dr. Joseph Bernard Josephson was San José's first specialist in orthopedics. He was born in Chicago and grew up in the wheatlands around Lewistown, Montana. After graduation from the University of California Medical School, he opened practice in San José in 1932.

Dr. Josephson served in both World Wars. He was on hand to care for wounded during the first U.S. Marine landing at Guadalcanal in 1942. He was only the third physician in O'Connor history to serve two successive terms as chief of staff (1952-53). He also headed the staff at San José Hospital and was the longtime director of orthopedic surgery at the County Hospital.

Dr. Phillips Thygeson was an internationally acclaimed eye specialist by the time he arrived in the Santa Clara Valley.

Born in St. Paul, Minnesota, in 1903, he moved to Palo Alto with his family in 1917 and earned his M.D. degree at Stanford University. He interned at Colorado General Hospital in Denver. He later became Chairman of the Department of Ophthalmology at Columbia University and Director of the Eye Institute of Presbyterian Hospital in New York City in the Thirties.

Dr. Thyleson entered private practice in parnership with Dr. Crowell V. Beard in 1946. A gifted diagnostician and teacher and brilliant researcher, Dr. Thygeson practiced 13 years before retiring to a position as Director of the Francis I. Proctor Foundation for Research in Ophthalmology at the University of California's San Francisco Medical Center.

Dr. Thygeson was instrumental in starting the Proctor Foundation, now the world's leading center for the study of ocu-

Dr. Phillips Thygeson, one of the first physicians in San Jose to limit his practice to eye diseases. Known through the medical world, Dr. Thygeson is regarded as the foremost authority on external diseases of the eye.

lar infections. It was financed by Mrs. Proctor as a memorial to her husband, a Boston ophthalmologist who shared with Dr. Thygeson a deep interest in trachoma.

Dr. Thygeson frequently tours the Indian nations of the Southwest to study and treat trachoma, an aviral disease afflicting persons of low economic status in arid regions.

The total of Santa Clara County physicians had grown to 1,800 by 1965, a figure that Benjamin Cory never would have imagined as possible when he stepped off the boat in Alviso 118 years before. But perhaps this is doing Dr. Cory an injustice. He had a way of setting his sights on the horizon and sparing no horses in getting there. He set standards that were sturdy guidelines to the hundreds of physicians who followed him through the years.

CHAPTER SEVEN

The Big Shake

NOTHING WAS SO RARE in the Santa Clara Valley as an athiest or a brick building standing firm that morning of April 18, 1906.

The Big Shake, California's mightiest earthquake, caught almost everyone in their slumber. The clock in San Jose's St. James Hotel stopped at 5:12.45 A.M. Pajama-clad residents jumped ont of their beds or catapulted out as the first tremblor lasted thirty seconds. All was quiet for ten seconds, then the earth shook for another twenty-five. A series of rolling waves made it difficult to stand up. Finally, the shifting along the San Andreas Fault ended.

In San José itself, the greatest damage occurred along Second Street north of San Fernando. The quake, measuring 8.25 in magnitude, collapsed buildings like houses of cards. Fires broke out. The new Hall of Justice was badly damaged. A score of guests were trapped when the new forty thousand dollar Vendome Hotel annex buckled, but only one was fatally injured. San José High School showed only as a hollow shell. All told, nineteen persons died in San José, eight thousand were left homeless and damage totaled more than three million dollars.

At O'Connor Sanitarium, plummeting chimneys punched gaping holes in the roof. The chapel was almost demolished. Plaster sprinkled the horrified patients in many rooms. But almost miraculously, most

St. Patrick's Catholic Church (above) was thirty years old at the time of the earthquake. The parish was founded in 1870, the second oldest in San Jose. The church, then at Eighth and Santa Clara Streets, was destroyed by the temblor (below) and workmen searched the ruins for valuable furnishings.

(Courtesy of San Jose Mercury-News)

90

of the structure was left intact and no one was seriously hurt. Sister Victorine, then the superior, declared that "the first dreadful shock almost swept us into eternity. But when we recovered our equilibrium, we found all the patients unharmed. The roof fell in here and there, but only on empty beds."

The County Hospital, reported the *San José Herald*, sustained heavy damage. "The main building lies in ruins. The recent brick addition where the kitchen was situated fell—and it was here that three of the patients were killed and seven badly injured. The main part of the building—the front—is very badly wrecked inside, the whole lower story is nearly two feet out of plumb and is liable to collapse any minute."

At fifteen-year-old Stanford University, the damage rose to an unbelievable five million dollars. The buildings, constructed in Romanesque style of a soft yellow stone, were easy prey to the rumbling earth. The university became a classic example of earthquake destruction. Massive gates framing the main quadrangle were shaken to the ground. The new library and gymnasium came down. And in the middle, the famous memorial church was in ruins. Air pressure created by the clock tower smashing through the roof blasted the mosaic off the church front. Yet, only two persons were killed on the campus. The lack of fatalities at the university pointed up a salient factor in the quake—the good fortune of the early hour. Had it hit five hours later when schools were in session and shops were crowded, the toll would have been too ghastly to contemplate.

The beautiful St. Patrick's Catholic Seminary in Menlo Park, a recent recipient of a fifty thousand dollar gift from Myles

The venerable Victory Theater on North First Street was shaken from stage to balcony. Such entertainers as Al Jolson and Bing Crosby performed on its stage before it was swept by a fire in 1965.

(Courtesy of San Jose Mercury-News)

P. O'Connor, was a shambles. In the Santa Cruz Mountains, ancient redwoods splintered and slid into creeks. At Kingsley Gulch at the foot of Loma Prieta, seventeen sawmill workers were buried by an earth avalanche.

The quake focused its cataclysmic might on San Francisco where the temblor and two days of fire killed 700 persons, wrecked 490 city blocks, destroyed 28,188 buildings, left 225,000 persons homeless and caused damage estimated at five hundred million dollars. The night before, celebrated tenor Enrico Caruso sang Don José in the opera

91

Valuable statuary tumbled to the floor of the Stanford University Memorial Chapel that morning of April 18, 1906. Heavy damage was caused when the clock tower crashed through the roof.

(Courtesy of San Jose Mercury-News)

Carmen and then adjourned to his room in the Palace Hotel. Minutes after the quake, the sleepy Caruso staggered onto Market Street, mumbling: " 'ell of a place, 'ell of a place. I never come back." And he never did. Relating the incident to friends later, he said, "I take Vesuvius anytime."

Charles W. Coe, a San José real estate man stopping over at San Francisco's Russ House, peered from a window of the hostelry moments after the quake. A woman popped her head out of the window in the next room and gasped, "What was that?" To which Mr. Coe replied wryly,

"That, my lady, was the first call to breakfast."

In the chaos that followed in the Golden Gate city, a million stories unfolded. Dr. Walter C. Alvarez, widely known physician and author, was interning at the City-County Hospital at the time. He recalled:

"The cruelest thing our none-too-bright superintendent immediately did was to throw out of the hospital everyone who could be gotten out of bed. His idea was that soon hundreds of injured persons would be brought in, and we would need beds for them. But emergency committees

STANFORD RESIDENCE

This Stanford University residence was literally propped up to keep it intact. The earthquake caused five million dollars in damage to the 15-year-old school.

(Courtesy of San Jose Mercury-News)

of physicians had quickly built tent hospitals here and there in the parks of the city, and for some time these makeshift places took care of all of the sick and injured. For a few weeks the central committee remained unaware of the fact that there existed in the city a large city hospital which was half empty."

The grimmest sight this eventful day, however, was Agnews State Hospital for the Insane. Nowhere in California had the impact of the quake been felt more in one spot than at Agnews. The imposing, four-story, eighteen-year-old Agnews Asylum housed some 1,080 patients at that time.

Including hospital employes, the quake killed 119. A massive dome that dominated the two block-long structure came thundering down when the walls, minus steel supports, crumbled.

News of the catastrophe quickly spread to Santa Clara, two miles away, where persons on the community's outskirts said they heard the roar of the crash. Although Santa Clara had its own problems, its 180,000-gallon water tank having collapsed and flooded the surroundings, some 100 university students ran all the way to the stricken asylum.

Sheriff William White of Los Angeles,

attending a lawmen's convention in San José, was one of the first at the scene. "The sight there was awful," he said. "The walls were standing, but the floors had all fallen in. Scores of insane persons were running about, unwatched and uncared for. I helped take out the body of Dr. Kelley, the assistant superintendent of the asylum, who had been instantly killed. A nurse who was also taken out of the ruins by me died a little later."

The highly respected Dr. E. A. Kelley had been hurled from his third floor apartment bed to the first story. His wife and children somehow survived. They were taken to O'Connor Sanitarium, as were many other injured persons. A dozen nurses and staff employes perished. Dr. Leonard E. Stocking, the superintendent, escaped out a window and down the fire ladder. Many reached safety by sliding down ropes improvised from knotted sheets. Angelina Kell, sister of County Coroner Bernard E. Kell, had fallen from the fourth floor to the basement of the administration building. Four dead bodies plummeted on top of her. Hours later, rescuers saw her free hand waving in the debris. She was pulled to safety with scarcely a mark on her.

Rumors that crazed persons were roaming the countryside around Agnews terrorized the populace. Although there was some truth to the stories, no untoward incidents ever came to light. On the asylum grounds, the more deranged patients were led from their padded cells and tied to trees with sheets and blankets. One inmate stood with glazed eyes and upraised arms, chanting: "Jesus of Nazareth is passing."

Searching the ruins for victims was a lugubrious chore, and not without inci-

Dr. James R. Curnow was an English-born physician who pioneered in designing of San Jose's sewer system and formation of the California state commission governing mental institutions.

dent. Dr. A. W. Hoisholt told the *San José Herald* a voice from the rubble attracted rescuers. "Quick, quick," came the words. Stone and timber were cast aside laboriously as a weak voice continued to repeat, "Quick, quick." Finally, searchers pulled away a last piece of debris to find a twisted cage, inhabited by a slightly injured parrot, the pet of Dr. Stocking. The parrot's command of the English language saved his life.

Two days after the quake, men still were raking through the debris. Then several heard a voice cry out, "Never mind me, get the others first." Digging frantically, they hauled a tattered patient out of the ruins. Rescuers believed it a miracle the man was alive—until a keeper ran up to reveal the patient had escaped from him only two hours before.

But no story was stranger than that of Dr. James R. Curnow. He had come to California for his health from England in 1872 with a brother, William, and they had engaged in Nevada County gold mining for awhile. He came to San José in 1874, enrolled at the University of the Pacific and was graduated in 1880. Curnow began his medical studies under two of San Jose's finest physicians, Drs. J. S. Potts and Robert Caldwell. He then completed his learning at Columbia University and Bellevue Hospital in New York City where he concentrated on public health and hygiene. When he returned to San Jose, he quickly put his training to work, noting the city's sewer system and health facilities were woefully inadequate. Dr. Curnow led in raising $500,000 to finance a new sewer system, a project that kept city engineer John H. Pieper busy for many years. Dr. Curnow, called the "Father of the Board of Health," also traced down cases of tuberculous meningitis which resulted in the destroying of 500 diseased milk cows.

During all this time, Dr. Curnow developed an interest in nervous diseases. He became an avid student of the English diagnostician, Dr. William Gowers, who with surgeon Victor Horsley conducted in 1887 the world's first successful spinal operation; and Dr. Jean Martin Charcot, France's foremost neurologist. Dr. Curnow's brilliance in the field won him an appointment in 1895 from Governor James H. Budd as a director of Agnews State Hospital. He rose to chairmanship of the board, which helped draw up the bill creating a State Commission of Lunacy. The commission laid the foundation for California's mental hospital system.

Ironically, Dr. Curnow himself began to suffer from emotional instability. Perhaps there was more fact than fiction to a remark by contemporary English neurologist Dr. Hughlings Jackson that "constant contact with patients suffering from nervous disorders makes everyone crazy, cynical or eccentric." Dr. Curnow entered Livermore Sanitarium and finally, on January 28, 1905, he was committed to Agnews Hospital. Then came the earthquake. Buffeted by the tremor and destruction all about him, Dr. Curnow regained his feet, located some medical instruments and began treating patients. "The terrific shock brought Dr. Curnow of this city . . . back to his normal mind," *The San José Mercury* reported. "He aided in the work as though nothing had ever been wrong.

Brick buildings took a beating from the quake. The upper story of the Native Sons Hall, Third and San Fernando Streets, was demolished. The lower floor, occupied by the Santa Clara Valley Wine Company, suffered little damage.

(Courtesy of San Jose Mercury-News)

Californians were proud of the magnificent new Agnews Asylum shown (above) shortly after its completion. Less than 20 years later, it was in ruins.

(Courtesy of Agnews State Hospital)

Makeshift shelters (foreground) accommodated hundreds of patients while others at Agnews were taken to Stockton State Hospital. The new Agnews hospital building opened in 1911.

(Courtesy of Agnews State Hospital)

WARNING!

NOTICE IS GIVEN that any person found Pilfering, Stealing, Robbing, or committing any act of Lawless Violence will be summarily

HANGED

MUIRSON & WRIGHT, PRINT.

Vigilance Committee.

A self-appointed vigilante named Coykendall printed up signs and tacked them all over San Jose immediately after the earthquake. He did it on his own after city officials ignored his warnings that looting would become a major problem. His fears were unfounded.

(Courtesy of San Jose Historic Landmarks Commission)

It is hoped the reaction will not place his mind again in a deranged condition." The newspaper's entreaty proved to no avail. The doctor died at Agnews on June 29, 1909.

Drs. Leonard E. Stocking, H. J. B. Wright and H. C. Brown directed relief operations at Agnews. Tents were pitched on lawns and soup kitchens set up. The makeshift arrangement accommodated some 860 patients until permanent facilities could be readied. The more violent patients were taken to Stockton State Hospital. It wasn't until 1911 that a new Agnews facility was erected, with a capacity of eighteen hundred patients.

In San Jose, Mayor G. D. Worswick announced solemnly: "There is scarcely a brick building standing that will not have to be rebuilt." He then warned looters a "heavy hand" would be used to deal with them. A San Josean appointed himself a one-man vigilante committee, printing up handbills proclaiming: "Notice is given that any person found pilfering, stealing, robbing, or committing any act of lawless violence will be summarily hanged." A *San José Mercury* editorial advised the despondent citizenry: "Keep a stiff upper lip, look the situation fairly in the face and discharge the duty that comes next in your hand."

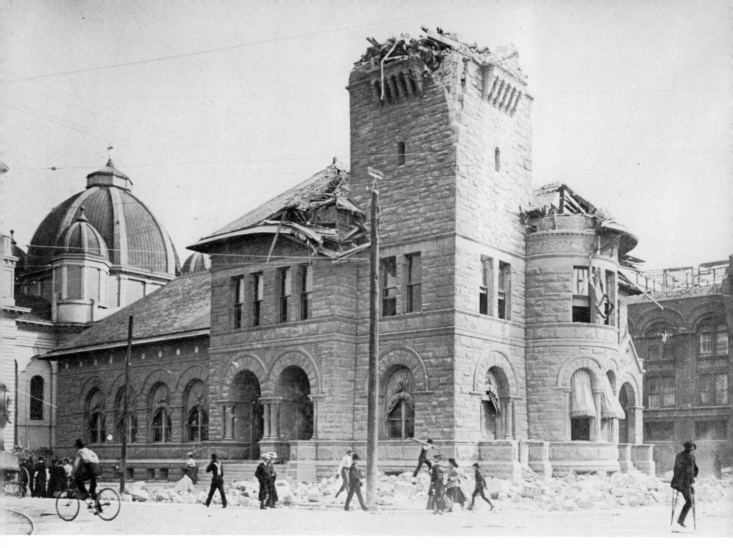

Pedestrians pick their way through the rubble in front of the San José Post Office. The spire was thrown to the ground and never replaced. The building was taken over by San José City Library in the 1930s.

(Courtesy of San Jose Mercury-News)

The Big Shake killed one guest, Thomas O'Toole, and injured twenty when it buckled the new Vendome Hotel Annex on North First Street.

(Courtesy of San Jose Mercury-News)

San José visitor Dr. M. W. Kapp authored an article for his hometown newspaper in Akron, Ohio. Dr. Kapp, who lived two blocks from the badly wrecked St. Patrick's Catholic Church, Ninth and Santa Clara Streets, wrote:

"I overheard one man say, 'Who can we thank that we survived this horror? Surely, God didn't bring this on because the churches are all destroyed and the breweries are all standing!' "

Dr. Kapp talked to a County Hospital official who related an incident during the temblor. An old patient had risen early and was peeling potatoes in the basement. The building began to shake, the roof fell and the second story above the kitchen collapsed. When attendants regained their senses, they rushed through dusty debris to the basement. There they found the old patient quietly peeling potatoes, oblivious of the pandemonium about him. In the women's ward, an elderly bedridden patient for years had rejected the opinion of County Physician George W. Fowler that there was no medical reason why she could not walk. But when the quake struck, she was the first one through the front gate.

At O'Connor Sanitarium, Sister Victorine moved fifty patients onto the lawn where tents were pitched. After a week the patients were transported to a temporary hospital established in the J. W. Chilton packing house at 385 North First Street. Dr. John D. Grissim, aided by Dr. E. F. Holbrook, the Rev. Anthony Mills and head nurse Mrs. C. J. Beggs, directed the emergency quarters which soon embraced 100 beds. Within twenty-four hours after the earthquake, refugees from San Francisco were en route to San José. "Some were covered with bandages and others were only partially clothed in their night garments," a *San José Mercury* reporter said. "Many were unconscious. The greater

The Hall of Justice, only a year old, was badly jarred by the earthquake. The sturdily built structure was renovated and served the community well until it was razed in 1963.

The collapse of Hobson's Clothing Store, on the west side of First Street at Post, killed one person and injured several others. Apartment dwellers next door suddenly found themselves exposed to the cool morning air.

(Courtesy of San Jose Mercury-News)

number were young women who had their limbs fractured or were crushed and burned." Among the refugees were scores of faculty members of St. Ignatius College, who were taken in by the Jesuits at Santa Clara College.

News of the plight of more than a thousand San Francisco physicians, many of whom had been burned out of their offices, reached their medical colleagues in the Santa Clara Valley. It was estimated half of the doctors in the Golden Gate city lost everything. The Santa Clara County Medical Society called a meeting at the home of Dr. J. J. Miller, Third and St. James Streets. The hat was passed and

three hundred and forty-five dollars were raised in a few minutes. The amount soon was tripled. The *Mercury* saluted the around-the-clock performance by San José doctors: "The spirit of every physician is deserving of the warmest praise . . . in almost every instance they refused fees from sufferers who applied to them for aid."

San José officials worked to avoid the fear that had gripped much of San Francisco, especially over the food and water supply. *Mercury* writer Patrick H. McEnery assuaged readers that the city had the situation well in hand. "While San Francisco has many homeless and hungry, the only way a man, woman or child could

100

starve in San José is by refusing to eat," he said. Businessman Henry Doerr, perturbed over stories of black marketing, pledged to sell 10,000 loaves of bread to the public for five cents each "and not a penny more."

The earthquake caught Californians in a rather jovial mood. The hit song in 1906 was "Meet Me in St. Louis, Louis, Meet Me at the Fair." High button shoes were the rage in women's fashions. A Princeton University president named Woodrow Wilson scorned the onset of the automobile age as encouraging socialism. "It has brought about a picture of the arrogance of wealth," he warned. But despite the advancement of America's industrial em-

pires, fears and superstitions still skulked in the minds of large segments of the population. Coupled with wild rumors and distorted stories, it was no wonder the Big Shake was attended by a multitude of bizarre happenings.

One woman was admitted to O'Connor Sanitarium two days after the quake when she and her husband imagined the temblor was returning and he had pushed her down the stairs in their rush for safety.

Socrates Kirk, a seventy-three-year-old capitalist and fruit grower, died a few hours after the quake from shock. The same cause ended the life of a supervisor at Agnews Hospital, Henry Angus Braden, a Coroner's inquest ruled. The *Herald*

The Unique Theater, of 24 East Santa Clara Street, San Jose, was wrecked by the rippling torsion along the San Andreas Fault in 1906. Because of the early hour, no one was injured by the shocks.

(Courtesy of San Jose Mercury-News)

reported the death of Joseph Nicholas Ghirardelli, a scion of the Bay Area chocolate manufacturing firm. A graduate of Santa Clara College, the fifty-three-year-old Ghirardelli was in Los Gatos that fateful morning. As lurid reports that San Francisco and Oakland had been wiped off the map filtered into the valley, he tried to engage transportation to the stricken area. Rushing pell mell about Los Gatos, he finally induced a chauffeur to brave the drive to his Oakland home for one hundred dollars. Arriving there he stepped toward his doorstep, then suddenly pitched forward. Ghirardelli fell into a coma and died a few days later, apparently of a heart attack.

An elderly San José physician, Dr. James T. Harris, was visiting in San Francisco during the quake. The next day his family was notified of his death. It was a puzzled Dr. Harris who walked into his house twenty-four hours later and inquired the cause of the sable wreaths on the door.

One of the weirdest incidents involved Judge Eugene M. Rosenthal, who shortly after the earthquake had been called to Agnews to help rescuers find the body of his brother, Leo. Finally, Judge Rosenthal pulled the body from the debris and he and several friends made a positive identification. Two days later, on Friday, the mourning family attended funeral services at the Home of Peace Cemetery off Monterey Road. The next day County Jailer G. Bryon Cottle called Dr. Stocking at Ag-

news to ascertain if Leo Rosenthal was really dead. Confirmation of death was given.

"That's funny," Cottle exclaimed, "I've got a fellow here who's been claiming he's Leo Rosenthal."

But Cottle wasn't convinced and an hour later called Judge Rosenthal, asking him to stop by the jailhouse. The aggrieved jurist agreed. Walking into the room, he immediately spotted his brother and rushed to embrace him. The thunderstruck judge, overcome with emotion, had to be helped to a chair. A few days later, gravediggers exhumed the body at Home of Peace Cemetery. It was identified as that of an Agnews inmate, Edward F. Joseph.

By April 30, a city inspection team had reached O'Connor Sanitarium. The new surgical section, the middle wing of the E-shaped building and the chapel were found to be unsafe and in need of repairs before they could be re-occupied. Judge and Mrs. O'Connor, shaken but unhurt by the quake, immediately ordered the reparation to begin. Contractor Edolph J. Shottenhamer was among crewmen renovating the structure, with costs exceeding fifty thousand dollars. Soon the institution's mission to care for the aged and the ailing was in full swing once more.

But stories of the Big Shake, the greatest natural trauma in California history, were on everyone's lips for many years afterward. And they always began at 5:12.45 A.M.

CHAPTER EIGHT

The Epidemic

In the fall of 1918, World War I was moving slowly toward its conclusion. While residents of the Santa Clara Valley had reasons to rejoice, little did they realize that a new danger was fast approaching. Headlines told the story: "Pacific Coast Braces for Possible Spanish Influenza Epidemic."

For six months, the world had sparred with the disease. As early as March, 1918, soldiers at Fort Riley, Kansas, had been hit by the influenza. Troops carried it abroad and soon every dot on the map save two was affected. Although Himalaya mountain hamlets and isolated Eskimo villages alike were decimated by the disease, somehow two South Atlantic isles, Tristan da Cunha and St. Helena, escaped. By the time the epidemic had run its course, twenty-one million persons were dead, including 850,000 in the United States. The influenza, which owes its name to ancient Italian astrologers who blamed the disease on the "influence" of the stars, was slow in arriving in the Santa Clara Valley. But once it found a toehold, there was nothing lacking in its impact. By October 8, the valley was almost in a state of seige.

Dr. Willard C. Bailey, San José city health director, and Dr. William Simpson, the county physician, met to discuss the crisis. Dr. H. C. Brown was appointed the city anti-influenza director. Dr. Bailey, a San José Normal School graduate who also became the city manager (1918-1920),

Dr. Willard C. Bailey, San Jose city health director during the influenza epidemic of 1918. He later was a San Jose city manager.

(Courtesy of San Jose Historic Landmarks Commission)

had sprung from a family renowned for its flocks of Angora goats and Persian sheep. But he had bypassed a career as a glove and robe manufacturer for medicine. On October 10, Dr. Bailey ordered all schools closed. The libraries and the College of the Pacific locked their doors. Church services were banned. Officials believed their quick action would pay off.

103

"Everyone wear masks to prevent spread of the germ and the disease will run its course in a short time," Dr. Brown said optimistically. But the influenza proved a foe far more formidable than even the most pessimistic observers could imagine.

On October 15, the *San José Mercury-Herald* reported 204 cases in a twenty-four hour period. Seven already were dead. Mrs. Mary Loustalet, 393 West San Fernando Street, lost three sons in one week and a fourth was in the hospital. Medical facilities were being strained. City Engineer Frank Nikirk ordered streets and sidewalks to be washed down. The huge fire trucks soon were flushing out the downtown area. Dr. Bailey suggested that banks and stores boil every coin and fumigate paper money at the end of each day. They quickly complied. Citizens were offered a formaldehyde formula to do the same in their homes. One official counted nineteen means of personal daily contact, from shaking hands to taking bus tokens from the driver. Efforts were increased to limit the contagion.

Two San José doctors, William Van Dalsem and A. L. Cochran, fell seriously ill from overwork and finally the virus itself. A few days later, Dr. Mark F. Hopkins was ailing.

"The doctor was very ill," Mrs. Hopkins recalls, "and I couldn't help him. We were expecting our first daughter and the day he became sick our nurse had to accompany me to the hospital. I was desperate because there was a great shortage of both doctors and nurses. Finally our minister agreed to stay with Dr. Hopkins until our nurse could return to care for him. Fortunately, he recovered after awhile."

With seventeen thousand American physicians in uniform, Santa Clara Valley officials were hard-pressed to find trained influenza fighters. In Santa Clara, Dr. George W. Fowler was swamped. "He carried on beyond the point of exhaustion," his daughter, Mrs. L. S. Prussia, remembers. "In one day, he saw five hundred twenty-five patients. He would stand on the running board and a friend, Chet Maloney, would drive. They had their long lists of calls to make and they made every one." On October 18, Mrs. Ada Hodgson, a nurse at Garden City Hospital, succumbed after catching the flu on her second case. Her death followed by only a month that of her brother, killed in combat in Europe.

The symptoms of Spanish influenza were a general malaise, usually accompanied by fever, slow pulse, drowsiness, sore throat and chest congestion. Sometimes there was double vision and dizziness. Most of all, the patient just looked sick. There were as many remedies as there were people to concoct them. One man wrote the *Mercury-Herald* he had found relief by "tossing flower of sulphur down the throat at the first symptom." Quinine, aspirin, and plain old soup had their supporters. Oldtimers advised snuff as a certain germ killer. Other people inhaled wood smoke or threw open windows to gulp more oxygen.

The Naval Training Station on Goat Island in San Francisco Bay clamped an absolute quarantine on four thousand men. Visitors were waved off at gunpoint. Every man was inoculated while the vaccine lasted. Drinking fountains were sterilized with blow torches and telephones sprinkled with alcohol every hour. Trainees marched and slept at least twenty feet from one another. No liberties were allowed that October, and indeed, the quarantine worked. Not a single case of influenza was reported on the island. When the epidemic quieted in early November the officers and men cheered the removal of the barriers. It was almost inevitable that when they arrived in San Francisco and other bay points, many quickly contracted the influenza.

On October 20, two persons died at O'Connor Sanitarium. One was a twenty-five-year-old woman from Monterey who had come to help nurse her younger brother convalescing from an appendectomy. The woman caught the influenza and it proved fatal three days later. Six others died in the valley as the County Nurses Association announced a grave problem—five pneumonia cases had been telephoned in that day and there was not a single trained person to answer the cries. The influenza especially ravaged the congested sections of the community. Dr. Bailey ordered health instructions to be printed in Italian since the Italian-American community was hard hit. An odd facet of the epidemic was that many persons refused to believe their illness was serious enough for hospitalization.

Dr. Bailey was distraught with the news twelve persons had died on October 23. He arranged to give the city's newsboys "a good old-fashioned bath." He again condemned all public gatherings. "This is no time for social meetings," he said sternly. "Twelve deaths occurred today and we can't tell what moment The Reaper will enter the home of those represented at these functions. If anyone has time for social gatherings, let it be used to nurse the sick." For those insisting on meetings, he urged the burning of formaldehyde candles.

Of the dozen dying on this black day, one was Dr. Joseph A. Regli, a forty-two-year-old O'Connor staff member and graduate of Santa Clara College. He contracted influenza and then pneumonia after maintaining an enervating day - and - night schedule.

Dark, overcast skies and a chilling ground fog added to the grimness of the picture as San José slowed to a virtual standstill. Judges closed their courtrooms. Sheriff A. B. Langford shut down the jail, evidently confident that potential lawbreakers were as sick as the police force.

The call went out for retired nurses and doctors to ameliorate a situation becoming more desperate by the hour. San Francisco and Oakland, themselves in trouble, received pleas from San José. On October 25, San Francisco dispatched a lone nurse —all it could spare. San Jose florist Jack Mieuli Sr., under the care of Dr. Edwin E. Porter, was seriously ill in his home. "There was a nurse, a Mrs. Rosasco, who came down from Oakland to help pull our family through," he said. "I don't know what we would have done without her."

The suffering city was given a great boost when the Holy Family Sisters volunteered their services. The Sisters of Notre Dame followed suit. At O'Connor Sanitarium, Sister Dolores went out on her own to help the stricken in their homes. Sister Clare tended the convent doorbell and telephone and helped with kitchen tasks while the heroic Holy Family nuns succored the ailing. Peter Dunne, a realtor, put his automobile at the sisters' disposal at 10:30 each morning and they were able to find a teenage boy to drive it. Edward McLaughlin, the esteemed banker (he was honored in the naming of McLaughlin Hall at the University of Santa Clara in 1957), informed the sisters to charge all supplies to him. The sisters gritted their teeth as they entered many homes. Often an entire family was stricken, with members huddled on couches or in beds, and no one able to prepare a simple broth. At day's end, the sisters dragged back to the convent and threw their soiled clothes in giant kettles of boiling water, stirring them with a long stick.

The order also opened up its Vine Street quarters as a community soup kitchen. They were joined by volunteers, including Mrs. Eugene A. Filipello, wife of the O'Connor staff physician, and her sister, Isabel de Saisset, who later willed funds for the de Saisset Art Gallery at the University of Santa Clara. The Holy Family nuns won official commendation from Dr. Bailey for their invaluable service.

On October 26, ninety-six died in San Francisco and seven in San José. Dr. Woods Hutchinson, internationally known expert on communicable diseases from New York, arrived in the valley to advise officials. He theorized the Spanish influenza virus, originally bred in Central Asia, broke loose to flood the world about every thirty years. The armies of Napoleon and George Washington suffered from the disease, he said, and its last previous appearance in the United States was in 1889-1890. He praised officials, pointing out their thirty deaths out of one thousand cases at this stage of the epidemic was only one-third of the ratio found in other cities.

Dr. Hutchinson's kind words during a fleeting appearance were soon forgotten as the crisis mounted. A Berkeley pharmaceutical firm announced development of an anti-influenza serum and it was sent immediately to San José. Physicians took it first themselves and made it available to patients. Its worth was not certain, but this was a world grasping at straws. A Second Street firm advertised a preventative — pea-sized sponges soaked in herbs inserted in the nostrils.

Stricken residents able to read the newspapers found little to cheer them. New York City counted 851 dead in one day. Philadelphia, rocked harder by the pestilence than any other city in the country, averaged 550 deaths a day for a fortnight as searchers canvassed for bodies house by house. In Washington, D.C., Missouri Congressman Jacob E. Meeker was near death. Despite his severe illness, the forty-year-old legislator and his fiancee decided to go ahead with marriage plans. The bedridden Meeker recited his vows through a flu mask. Seven hours later he was dead, the first congressional fatality. Franklin D. Roosevelt, thirty-six, the ambitious Under Secretary of the Navy, was very ill. Brigadier General Charles A. Doyen, Quantico (Virginia) Marine Base commandant and recently returned hero of Chateau-Thierry, became the highest ranking military man to succumb. Dr. Victor C. Vaughan, assistant U.S. Surgeon General and head of the Army Communicable Disease Section, noted that the disease especially attacked big, strong men rather than children or the elderly. "The husky male," he said, "either made a speedy and rather abrupt recovery or was likely to die . . . Infection, like war, kills young, vigorous, robust adults."

Influenza kits were under production. They included such items as morphine, aspirin, quinine, rubbing alcohol, pajamas, masks, hot water bottles, fly paper, soap, screens and pneumonia jackets (heavily padded vests designed to keep patients warm in cold rooms). The sports page told of canceled football games. And movie houses were silent, their billboards still

Ruby Hannaford, who was fatally stricken by the 1918 influenza epidemic only a month after her graduation from the O'Connor Sanitarium Nursing School. She was buried in full nurse's uniform.

(Courtesy of Earl Hannaford)

advertising Will Rogers in "Laughing Bill Hyde," William S. Hart in "The Border Wireless," and Dorothy Gish in "Battling Jane."

Fifty-five students were so ill at the University of Santa Clara that they were shipped EN MASSE to O'Connor Sanitarium where the superior, Sister Zoe Schieswehl,

and nurses like Ruby Hannaford and Viola Gardner struggled to accommodate them. Reflecting on those days, Miss Gardner said:

"The Sanitarium was so crowded we had patients in the front parlors and even in the hallways. The worst cases, including some of the Santa Clara boys, were put in the isolation building. The doctors could hardly stand on their feet. Often only three out of ten nurses were well enough to work. The people, by the time they were hospitalized, occasionally were beyond help. The sick were arriving at one door and the hearse took away the dead at the other. A Portuguese boy from Santa Clara was brought in smiling and joking one morning. Two days later, he was gone. The doctors tried so hard but no one really knew what to do."

Lloyd J. Rodey of San José was one of the fifty-five Santa Clara students brought to O'Connor's, although prank-loving classmates made him wonder if the trip was necessary. Rodey, who had fainted in the campus chapel, awoke to find himself laid out on the floor with tall, brightly burning candles placed around him.

"The hospital was so overcrowded when we arrived that the sisters turned over their own living quarters to the patients." Rodey said. "I was one of those placed in the chapel. Dr. Gerlach would appear at the door and say, 'Salts [laxative] for everybody.' Some of the fellows, rather than take it, poured it down the heating register. I was in bed two weeks and then I helped out as an orderly for awhile."

Clement J. Schuh of San José, a strapping six-foot two-hundred pounder, was the only university student claimed by the flu. "Schuh was in the hall outside the chapel," Rodey recalled. "I could see the doctors rushing to his side, but they were unable to save him."

On October 27, Mary E. Dougherty McGinty, wife of O'Connor staff doctor Arthur T. McGinty, died. Dr. McGinty, ill himself, tried in vain to save his wife who caught the flu while caring for their ailing son, Arthur Jr. The death of Mrs. McGinty, a graduate of the College of Notre Dame, saddened an already anguished community. A Santa Clara mother lost two sons in two days. Dr. Bailey appealed for more nurses. "If we could have the help of just twenty women at once, it would mean the saving of many lives," he informed a *Mercury - Herald* reporter. A Red Cross worker was in despair as she added: "I cannot describe the conditions. They are simply tragic . . . The nurses are worn out. Unless the women of the city lend assistance the death rate will be something unimaginable."

Epidemiologists warned the West Coast that any moment it would feel the peak assault of the disease. On October 28, the San Francisco death count was seventy-seven. The recent warnings of a baseball player turned Evangelist, Billy Sunday, were materializing. "San Francisco," he had said in a recent visit, "was going to hell so fast it ought to be arrested for speeding." There were 111 dead in Los Angeles this day and fourteen in San José. The City Council put teeth in a Board of Health order, authorizing fines of up to one hundred dollars for any San Joséans caught in public without an influenza mask. Forty arrests were made the first day. The fact that many citizens found store supplies of the masks exhausted held no sway with sober-faced policemen.

The deaths of eight more persons on the 29th and over-capacity hospital conditions prompted Dr. Bailey to call an urgent meeting of city officials. Emergency facilities were needed. President Morris E. Dailey of San José Normal School offered his intermediate training building for a hospital and the city gratefully accepted. Twenty-four hours later, the hospital was operational. Faculty members Elizabeth McFadden, Margaret M. Twombly and J. C. Elder helped O'Connor staff physician, Newell H. Bullock, both at the bedside and in the improvised kitchen. At the emergency's zenith, seventy nurses were toiling in two shifts.

Pneumonia became the greatest fear in the wake of the first wave of Spanish influenze, claiming San José's Milton Blackmore, twenty-three, on October 30 in San Francisco. Young Blackmore had been the first man in the city to try to enlist at the outbreak of the war, but he was rejected because of flat feet. He immediately went to San Francisco to go to work at a war industry, the Union Iron Works.

The victim's brother Raymond, then only fourteen, was the sole member of a family of seven on his feet in their Settle Avenue residence. The busy youngster wore a mask as he did his chores, closely following the advice of family doctor C. E. Hablutzel (the son-in-law of pioneer physician Benjamin Cory). "I was the cook, chambermaid, bottle washer and what-have-you," remembers Raymond Blackmore, later San Jose's police chief who was blessed with such good health that he served thirty-seven years on the force without missing a day's work.

Doctors at Camp Fremont's military hospital near Palo Alto on October 31 hailed a new discovery to kill off the elusive influenza germ. "Coaguline has been found to be a positive cure," the *Mercury-*

No, it wasn't a highwaymen's convention. Conforming with a city ordinance requiring all citizens to wear masks during the 1918 influenza epidemic, the San Jose chapter of the Native Sons of the Golden West held its regular November meeting in front of the McKinley statue in St. James Park.

(Courtesy of San Jose Historic Landmarks Commission)

Herald quoted camp medics. " . . . It thickens the blood and prevents it from filling the lungs." Although subsequent use failed to justify the enthusiasm, it served to underline a treacherous characteristic of the disease. The lungs of a dying patient filled with fluid, suffocating the victim and causing the entire body to turn blue-black. Such patients were said to have died of the "black flu."

Mrs. Maude Dillon Haynes of Saratoga, a 1915 O'Connor Nursing School graduate, was at Camp Fremont when the epidemic felled nineteen hundred servicemen. The camp, whose physicians included Frederick Gerlach and A. S. J. Smith of San José, was like military posts all over the country where overcrowding contributed heavily to the death toll. "There were only two nurses for twenty-five tents and each tent housed five or six cots," Mrs. Haynes recalls. "We lost many boys because the Army treated every patient identically, despite the fact that the influenza affected each person differently. Another problem was that physicians skilled in other phases of medicine, or those doctors simply with a higher rank, directed the influenza section. Dr. Smith, for example, was an ear, nose and throat specialist. Yet, he was sent to our influenza area."

On October 31, Dr. Bailey urged San José to forget its normal Halloween festivities on account of the epidemic. There was many a fence gate and store window that escaped the goblins on that chilly autumn holiday of 1918. The next day, the epidemic appeared to have passed its crest with only four deaths reported in the city. But on November 2, it proved fatal to another physician, Dr. William J. Fretwell. A highly respected practitioner, Dr.

Fretwell was only fifty years old. Anna Delmue, a nurse for Dr. Louis V. Saph, contracted the disease and died. In Santa Clara, Mrs. Henry L. Warburton saw thirteen funeral corteges pass her home in one day.

And at O'Connor, Ruby Hannaford lay seriously ill. Then on November 3, five days after her incapacitation, she was dead. The passing of the twenty-one-year-old O'Connor honor graduate left the sanitarium in a state of shock. Dr. E. F. Holbrook shook his head. "She was a wonderful nurse," he said. Her colleagues were numb. Only the cries of the suffering in the overloaded institution kept the heart-sick nurses at their posts. Miss Hannaford had personified the bravery of the doctors, nurses and lay volunteers who fought this phantom virus. Her body was buried in full nurse's uniform at Oak Hill Cemetery.

Despite the pervading gloom, San Joséans found time to laugh. The *Mercury-Herald* published pictures of bank guards ignoring masked customers, pondering the problem of how to recognize a legitimate holdup man. Haberdasher Jay McCabe was joshed for liking the flu masks, which covered an ample nose. In San Francisco, fashionable women wore harem-type veils called "yashmaks." And quarantined youngsters chirped this little ditty:

I had a little bird
It's name was Enza,
I opened the window
And in-flu-Enza.

The city listed six dead on November 4, nine on each of the next two days, and then only two on November 7. "La grippe," as it was known in some parts of the country, was running its course. After a fatality count of six hundred seventy-nine for one week in San Francisco, officials there conceded the disease was waning. Church services were approved in San José for Sunday, November 10, although the schools remained closed. An altar was improvised in the entrance of St. Joseph's Church, and parishioners prayed on the lawn and in the street. At midnight, health officials broke into broad smiles. For the first day in five weeks, not a single fatality was noted.

Few days in a valley's long history dawned brighter than November 11, 1918. For the first time in more than a month, a news story had pushed the influenza out of the top headlines. Citizens cast off their masks and paraded merrily through the streets. World War I had ended. And the pandemic appeared on its last legs. The flu, although it lingered on in scattered places throughout the winter, no longer held the populace in a state of terror. At the final count, almost two hundred graves bore mute testimony to the valley's ordeal.

Historian A. A. Hoehling, who made an intensive study of the 1918 malady, outlined his fear of the epidemic. "Had it continued its mathematical rate of acceleration . . . civilization could have disappeared within a few more weeks," he wrote.

Although World War I had ended, the war against the influenza virus continued. In 1933, the virus was isolated by scientists in London. Soon the virus' strains were identified. In 1951, Iowa researchers tried a new tack. They exhumed the frozen bodies of 1918 flu victims in Alaska, packed the lung sections in ice and returned them to Iowa in an effort to infect laboratory animals. But alas, the virus had disappeared. Where it went or if it will re-appear in such force again are mysteries. Many doctors today believe anti-biotics would prevent a lot of the deaths. They theorize that a secondary bacterial infection such as pneumonia—not the flu—was the actual killer. But almost a half century after the Great Epidemic of 1918 no one can say for certain the virulent virus will not return.

The entire enrollment of the O'Connor Sanitarium Nursing School in 1910. Two male nurses were enrolled, Louis McQuaid (left) and Aloysius McQuaid. Irene Flanagan (third from right in third row) later entered the Daughters of Charity. She currently is on assignment at O'Connor Hospital.

CHAPTER NINE

Nurses in the Attic

BEFORE FLORENCE NIGHTINGALE, "nursing" was an occupation shunned by any well-born woman.

A hospital was a pesthole where people came to die and often drunkards and slatterns were charged with their care. But the Nightingale influence, coupled with the antiseptic techniques introduced by Joseph Lister and Ignace Semmelweiss, eventually revolutionized hospital cleanliness and transformed nursing into an honored and respected profession.

As late as 1890, there were only thirty-five nursing schools in the United States. By 1900 the number had risen to 432. Sister Raphael Jones, O'Connor Sanitarium superior (1894-98), made s w e e p i n g changes during her tenure in the young institution. Foremost among her projects was the founding of the O'Connor School of Nursing in February, 1898. It was one of the very first such programs initiated in Northern California, and previous to any in the southern half of the state. O'Connor's also was the first Catholic nursing school in California.

Some of the seven girls enrolled in the first class dropped out, but others came in and in 1900 the first graduation counted nine nurses. The school archives identify them as Mary Brinsmead, Annie Carr, Mary Conroy, Josephine Good, Hortence Keane, Mary Satterfield, Mae Shipley, Mary X. Mooney and George McClellan. The school, consisting mainly of bedside

and "medicine cabinet tutoring" from physicians and the sisters—on the job training in its purest form—graduated no one in 1901 or 1902 and only one nurse in each of the next two years. But under Sister Dolores Carlos, the first superintendent of nurses, the school's reputation grew and in 1906 it was incorporated under the name, San José Sanitarium Training School.

The life of the nursing students was arduous and only the strongest lasted. Their hardships by today's standards are incredulous. Needing only a grammar school education at first, they worked 12-hour shifts, from 7 to 7 day or night, with a half-hour off for lunch, an hour in mid-afternoon and a half-hour for dinner. The work week was six and a half days, with a 10 p.m. curfew. Twice a week during "free" time they attended classes taught by the doctors. They learned such duties as applying leeches to a patient or how to properly blister the skin with counter-irritants.

Women nurses lived in the attic above the surgery department and took meals in the basement kitchen, with a long helical stairway connecting the floors. Male nurses, although few in number, lived in the basement.

"We had to stand tall for inspection when we reported on duty," remembers Charles A. Reimer of Los Gatos, a 1912-15 student. "Even our fingernails were inspected. I used to get $20 a month, including board, room and laundry. There

Flag-waving nurses from O'Connor Sanitarium take part in liberty bond parade in 1917. They are marching west on Santa Clara Street between Fourth and Fifth Streets.

(Courtesy of Earl Hannaford)

was no paid vacation. We often would be so tired in the evening we'd fall asleep during school lectures. When we were assigned as a special nurse for a patient immediately after surgery, we would have to sit up all night. The next night we could nap on a cot in the patient's room. The sisters were strict, but they were wonderful to us. I used to ask one, Sister Mary Louis (superior, 1914-17), for an advance on my wages upon occasion. She would call me aside and reach into her pocket for a five dollar gold piece. We were always paid in gold in those days. I would always pay it back to her directly so as not to upset the sister in charge of the payroll."

Nurses wore the old blue and white striped material, with white collars and cuffs. Full skirts reached almost to the floor. They were topped by full bib aprons. The caps were fluffs of white organdy trimmed with ruching.

The school maintained rigid discipline. Nurses unable to conform to the regimen were dismissed. The school's early registers cited reasons for individual expulsions: "Caught smoking; second offense — dismissed," "light-minded, late hours" and "incompetent." Deportment and cleanliness meant as much on a report card as nursing skill. Often, nurses would go into private homes to care for a patient over many weeks. The students then were graded by the families.

Mrs. Morgan Dillon Baker, a public-spirited woman whose husband was a noted O'Connor radiologist, was almost expelled before her graduation as a nurse in 1912 because of a practical joke. "I was a senior and I left some candy doused with pepper for the new students," Mrs. Baker said shortly before her death in 1965. "The superintendent severely reprimanded me and said, 'How can we expect you to be a re-

114

liable and dependable nurse if you are this frivolous?' Fortunately, I was allowed to stay. Despite the long hours and hard work, the nurses did very little complaining. We started many friendships there, not only with other nurses but with patients. In those days, a patient would stay two to four weeks and we developed close relationships, something that is hard to do today."

The young nursing Lucilles had little time for merry Oldsmobiles, but they made the most of their leisure time. Mrs. Maude Dillon Haynes of Saratoga, California, remembers the problems of extracurricular activities: "Dates were very difficult not only because we had so little time off, but because we rarely knew very far in advance when it could come. Usually we would go dancing. There was a dance hall on Market Street on the location later occupied by the Bigley Ambulance Company. We had to catch the 9:30 p.m. interurban car back to the sanitarium. Sometimes, when we couldn't get back in time, we would have to sneak in. The girls all looked out for each other. We spent so much time together we were like sisters in one big family."

The program was renamed the O'Connor Sanitarium Training School in 1910. The course had been increased to three years in 1906 and stayed there until 1922 when it was cut to twenty-eight months. In 1942, eight months of senior training were added, and in 1945 the course was officially set at three years. A nurses' alumnae association was organized on October 14, 1908, for the "purpose of (1) providing financial help for graduates, (2) advancing standards of the profession, (3) improving the O'Connor program and (4) promoting good fellowship."

The cramped attic quarters went out in 1916 when a separate residence was built behind the sanitarium. An addition in 1925 enabled the residence to accommodate sixty-five nurses. The building stood the school in good stead until the spring of 1954 when the new $1,020,000 structure with a 125-nurse capacity opened on Forest Avenue. The three-winged building showed off classrooms, offices, an auditorium and living facilities. The streamlined patio, glassed-in recreation room, sewing rooms and modern laboratories were a far cry from the rustic accommodations of that first class in 1898.

Changing times lightened the work of the nurses, but put new emphasis on education and intelligence. By 1927, nurses were working ten-hour shifts in the day and twelve hours at night, with one day off a week. Two years of high school were an admission requirement. In 1928, a high school diploma was deemed necessary. Twenty years later, all classes and hospital duty was packed in a forty-hour week, cut-

A view of the nurses' quarters in the attic of O'Connor Sanitarium about 1912. The nurses felt they had spent half of their lives climbing the sturdy circular stairway to and from their living area.

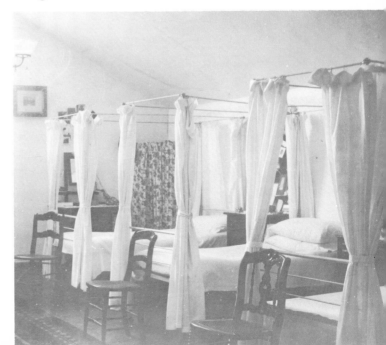

The O'Connor Sanitarium kitchen about 1910 was a busy place. Besides the preparation of food, it was used for sterilizing surgical instruments. Hot water was carried from the basement kitchen in kettles to other parts of the building.

Sweeping architectural lines characterize O'Connor Hospital Nursing School, built in 1954. The $1,020,00 structure accommodates up to 125 nurses. The school was founded in 1898.

ting almost in half the work-study time of the early graduates. The school, first accredited by the Board of Nursing Examiners in 1917, rose in its field until by 1949 it was rated in the upper quarter of all nursing institutions in the United States. Its first lay instructor was Katherine Coleman, hired to teach nursing obstetrics in 1925. By 1954, the school had five full-time instructors, plus a librarian, housemothers and secretaries. The school passed intensive inspection to gain accreditation by the National League of Nursing in January, 1958. And it has successfully passed all the tests for accreditation by the California State Board of Nursing Education and Nurse Registration.

In 1946, the school recognized that nursing education embraces knowledge drawn from the natural and behavioral sciences, liberal arts and the truths of theology and philosophy, all applied to the health needs of the patient. The healing art was one best synthesized with a broad education. The nurses began attending classes at San José State College in 1946 and later moved to the University of Santa Clara. Soon one-third of their curriculum was devoted to courses other than in their medical field, mostly in the freshman year.

O'Connor's realized the broadening scope of the nurses' profession. Affiliation with the County Hospital for nurse training in obstetrics and private patient care was established as early as 1936. Later, students learned psychiatric nursing at Agnews State Hospital and how to care for the well child at St. Elizabeth's Day Home in San José.

O'Connor graduated thirty nurses in 1965, the school's all-time largest class in peacetime. It produced 795 nurses over the first sixty-seven years. Exemplary of the

Mrs. Ethel Townsend Bull, a 1907 graduate of O'Connor Sanitarium Nursing School, was the granddaughter of pioneer physician Dr. John Townsend. She was employed as a nurse at the sanitarium for many years.

(Courtesy of Mrs. Arthur Townsend)

school's caliber of instruction was the 1964 examinations for state registration in which O'Connor students, matched against fifty-seven other California institutions, scored FIRST in surgical, FOURTH in psychiatric and TWELFTH in obstetric nursing.

The school, whose graduates represent many races and religious creeds, long has sought to blend with its educational objectives the most important ingredient of all — the nurse's sensitivity to a patient's total physical, spiritual, emotional and social needs.

Such sensitivity, as it is today, was a nursing goal at O'Connor Hospital in 1898.

Buggies and "horseless carriages" parade south on Market Street in San Jose on the Fourth of July, 1909, a few days after the death of philanthropist Myles P. O'Connor. The tower at Market and Santa Clara Streets illuminated the downtown area for 34 years until its collapse in 1915.

(Courtesy of San Jose Historic Landmarks Commission)

CHAPTER TEN

Passing of a Philanthropist

JUDGE AND MRS. O'CONNOR watched their art collection grow until it was obvious it no longer could be accommodated at the sanitarium. In 1898, they decided to make a gift of the collection, already numbering 425 pieces and valued in excess of $250,000, to the City of San José. It was an offer tainted with frustration. What started out as a simple gesture of philanthrophy extended over three years of complexities, climaxing in the after-glow of a President's assassination.

Attorney Nicholas Bowden, representing the O'Connors, informed city officials the art collection was theirs provided it could be adequately housed in a gallery on the Normal School campus. It was estimated such a facility would cost twenty thousand dollars. Civic-minded residents, overjoyed at the offer, immediately made plans to raise the money by public subscription. An initial wave of pledges prompted merchant O. A. Hale to go to Sacramento in March, 1898, to sound out Governor James H. Budd. Budd said he foresaw no objections to the gallery's location on state property.

"I consider the state very lucky to be proffered so munificent a gift. I congratulate the City of San José on its good fortune," Budd said. "I have no doubt the citizens will provide the necessary funds to construct a suitable building for the reception of this magnificent collection."

The *San José Mercury* shared Budd's delight:

"San José cannot afford to ignore so splendid an offer. Such an elegant art building would give San José a prestige such as no other city on the Pacific Coast except San Francisco enjoys . . . The money will be subscribed. The project is chiefly in the hands of the ladies of San José and with them there can be no such thing as failure."

The ladies indeed were spearheading the effort. The San José Art Association formed a special "Committee of One Hundred." Other women's clubs lent a hand. But the citizens were loath to contribute. While the campaign seemed to be dragging, a San José magazine called *The Sketch* on December 16, 1899, hummed an optimistic tune:

Patients found a casual, home-like atmosphere when they checked into the reception room of O'Connor Sanitarium about 1920.

Mrs. Myles O'Connor lived in only a small apartment at the Sanitarium after her husband's death. She kept busy carrying out many of the philanthropic projects he had started.

"San José has in prospect the finest art museum west of Chicago. Mrs. M. P. O'Connor, known all over the state for her benefactions, has donated to the City her magnificent collection of paintings gathered from every part of the world. She is an art critic of taste and excellence and her selections have been remarkable for their high grade and character. The women of San José are raising the funds to erect a building suitable to house the O'Connor collection of art and their success has been phenomenal. There is no question but that a very few months will see the cornerstone laid for the new art gallery."

The magazine's enthusiasm was matched only by its lack of foresight. The turn of the century did little to awaken the community's sense of culture. The O'Connors, disappointed at the city's temporizing, decided finally San José had failed to live up to its end of the bargain.

Several years before, they had become close friends with Sister Julia McGroarty, the provincial superior of all the Sisters of Notre Dame de Namur in the United States. When the O'Connors learned Sister Julia was founding a new institution in Washington, D.C., called Trinity College, they offered her the collection. She graciously accepted. Since they wanted to contribute to the new school's construction, they decided to also erect a gallery. Although Sister Julia died in 1901, the O'Connors continued negotiations with the new president, Sister Lidwine, and agreed to finance the three-story central wing of the main building, which was named O'Connor Hall. The hall and the art gallery cost the O'Connors more than $200,000 and could not be duplicated today for several million dollars.

The art treasures arrived at Trinity College in forty-five redwood cases, insured for $250,000. In April, 1904, the O'Connors made the long journey to the nation's capital to prepare for the gallery's grand opening. It coincided with the college's first commencement in June. The judge, blind but uncomplaining, patiently waited out the two months before the ceremonies while his wife helped with the arrangements. Besides almost a hundred oil paintings, the collection included water colors, engravings and etchings, sculptures in crystallized Carrara marble, mosaics and bronze pieces.

San José's loss was the capital's gain. It wasn't the first time the valley had lost a chance to grow a cultural arm. General Henry M. Naglee, pioneer San Francisco banker and Civil War veteran who commanded a brigade under General McClellan, had made San José his home in 1865. His sumptuous residence was located on a 140-acre property bounded by Santa Clara Street on the north, the Coyote River on the east, William Street on the south and Tenth Street on the west. During trips to Europe, he collected art pieces

The main showroom of the O'Connor Art Gallery at Trinity College, Washington, D.C. These and many other valuable art pieces were offered by Myles O'Connor to the City of San Jose. But the city lost them when it could not raise enough money for its own gallery.

Trinity College, Washington, D.C., as it appeared about the time of Myles O'Connor's death in 1909. O'Connor Hall, the central wing of this building, was a gift from the California philanthropist. It houses the valuable O'Connor Art Gallery today.

and learned of wines. The general started making his own brandy and it was prized for its excellence. Before his death in 1886, Naglee offered his art collection to the community. When there was no response, it was turned over to the Crocker Art Gallery in San Francisco. The entire collection was destroyed in the 1906 earthquake-fire.

Although San Joséans had pledged more than seven thousand dollars toward a Normal School art gallery, only $3,600 in cash lay in the bank. It still was there in May, 1901, when President William McKinley visited the city, stopping over at the Vendome Hotel while parades and dinner parties toasted the occasion. McKinley won over his hosts completely and the news of

an assassin's attempt upon his life in Buffalo, N.Y., four months later stunned San José residents.

An anarchist had pumped two bullets into the President at close range. In an era when physicians advertised daily in the press, Dr. George W. Seifert raised few eyebrows when he discussed the President's condition with a *San José News* reporter the day after the shooting. Noting McKinley had been shot twice in the chest, with the bullets missing the vital organs, Dr. Seifert commented that "the only real danger was from blood poisoning." But McKinley's condition deteriorated and seven days after the shooting, Dr. Seifert said bluntly: "The chances of recovery are remote, although he has a slight chance." The Santa Clara physician even predicted death within twenty-four hours, but a cautious reporter held it out of his story. McKinley did die the next day, September 14.

Bereaved San Joséans seeking a way to honor the President's name fell behind a suggestion by the Rev. Robert E. Kenna, S.J., president of Santa Clara College. His plan was to build a monument, using the $3,600 in cash left over from the abortive O'Connor art gallery drive as a launching pad. The art association met at the home of Mrs. E. O. Smith and endorsed the idea. In eight days, the fund had risen to $8,463. By October 25, it was up to $13,728 and the project's success was assured. The monument was unveiled in St. James Park

on the exact spot he had addressed the community the previous May. An impassioned speech by Father Kenna highlighted the unveiling ceremony. Mrs. O'Connor never passed the monument without feeling she and her husband had unwittingly played a part in its being.

Outside of the 1904 trip to Washington, D.C., the O'Connors rarely left the sanitarium after 1902. Sightless and aging, the judge still made the most of his last seven years. He would stroll in the grape arbor daily, guiding himself by means of a long smooth rope strung along the path. Mrs. Minnie Farrell, a practical nurse, would read to him. Occasionally, a young violinist named Stanley Sprung, stopped by to play. So as not to burden sanitarium personnel, arrangements were made for the

A mountain of flowers grown by Santa Clara Valley residents forms a backdrop for President McKinley during his visit to St. James Park in San Jose in May, 1901. He was assassinated two months later and the community, using leftover O'Connor Art Gallery drive funds, built the statue in his honor in the park.

(Courtesy of San Jose Historic Landmarks Commission)

The gravestone of Myles P. O'Connor in Santa Clara Catholic Cemetery, erected by his wife in 1909. She also had built a memorial gate at the cemetery in his honor. O'Connor died of a stroke at the age of 86.

Bon Secour Sisters, a nursing order from France, to give O'Connor special care. Each sister would come from abroad and stay one year.

His uncomplaining posture was an inspiration to acquaintances. Mrs. O'Connor confided in her diary that his "affliction is a greater sorrow than he feels it to be." On bright spring Sunday afternoons, the St. Joseph's School Band and Bugle Corps —which the judge had outfitted previously —would play concerts on the sanitarium lawn for his especial enjoyment. In 1907, Santa Clara College conferred upon him an honorary degree of Doctor of Philosophy.

In the judge's declining years, "Mrs. O'Connor was ever at his side, ministering to him night and day," the *Mercury* noted. "Her devotion was most sublime, and of a depth and intensity seldom witnessed."

Myles Poore O'Connor died at 12:30 A.M. on June 9, 1909. Attending physician J. Underwood Hall Jr. attributed his death to the third of a series of apoplectic strokes. He was eighty-six.

Edward McLaughlin, O'Connor's friend of fifty-eight years standing, summarized the judge's life:

"He always listened to the call of the unfortunate and distressed. He was kind, courteous, considerate and possessed a noble and refined character. He was particularly interested in orphans, and was always planning in their behalf. His greatest pleasure was in visiting them and looking after their welfare. Not only did he give money freely to help the needy and suffering, but he did noble deeds as well. He was always genial, always thoughtful of others, even under grievous affliction. His patience was almost marvelous. He never complained and his mind was calm, serene and unclouded to the last. He was a wonderful mind; he was a man of great depths, possessed a vast fund of information, and he took pride in his fine library. He leaves ample funds for his widow to complete any charitable undertakings which he may have planned. He was an honor to his state and a worthy example of a large-hearted, unselfish and benevolent citizen who was actuated solely by the desire to benefit humanity. This county and state may well be proud of the record of Judge Myles P. O'Connor."

The funeral was one of the most impressive in valley history. Mourners came from throughout California. The Catholic Archbishop's office attended en masse. Representatives of agencies that had benefitted from his philanthropy filled half the church. "This life which has gone from us has been lived in the open," eulogized Archbishop Patrick W. Riordan. "I can tell you nothing that you do not know. I can praise him no more than you can yourselves . . . He was a man neither bought nor led. He stood for the highest in morality, law and order. All that he had he held in sacred trust. One of the greatest misfortunes of the present day and one reason there is to much antagonism in those possessing wealth is because of their misuse of its power, and its diversion to their own selfish ends instead of using it for the good of God and of humanity . . . The things that pass are of small value. The things which last through eternity are of infinite value. It was thus the deceased viewed his own life and so prepared his soul for eternity. His motto was the Divine common, 'Love God with thy whole heart and soul and love thy neighbor as thyself.'"

The burial was in an underground

marble crypt in Santa Clara Catholic Cemetery. The words, "Thou hast loved justice and hated inquiry" were inscribed on the stone. Later, his widow had built the large O'Connor Memorial Arch at the cemetery entrance. O'Connor's death was reported in depth by the San José, San Francisco, Grass Valley, Sacramento and Missouri press. "Oldest Alumnus of St. Louis University Law School Dies," read a headline in a St. Louis newspaper.

If O'Connor died with a regret, it was that he and his wife were childless. They tried at various times to adopt nephews and nieces, but without success. Excepting Mrs. O'Connor, the largest individual stipulation in his will was $50,000 bequeathed to a brother, Jerome, of Peipers Fork, Tennessee. A total of $145,000 was meted out to relatives, including $10,000 to a nephew the judge had never seen. He endowed the Los Gatos Novitiate and Notre Dame Institute with $10,000 each and the Daughters of Charity of O'Connor Sanitarium with $5,000.

O'Connor lived only two months shy of fifty years in California. His philanthropies stretched from coast to coast. His larger civil and ecclesiastical charities were familiar to everyone, but many of his smaller gifts and favors were not revealed until years after his death. Indeed, some no doubt remained forever a secret between the donor and the recipient. Mrs. O'Connor confided later that of all his benefactions, none gave him more satisfaction than that of the sanitarium.

His generosity to the orphans of the Notre Dame Institute, Trinity College, the Young Men's Institute, St. Patrick's Seminary, Santa Clara College, Los Gatos Novitiate, the Daughters of Charity of St. Vincent de Paul and the Sisters of

Mrs. Amanda O'Connor's love of flowers was evident in the entranceway to her apartment in a corner of O'Connor Sanitarium about 1918. After her death in 1926, the apartment was used as a sisters' residence.

Notre Dame de Namur has been recorded. But without fanfare he also gave $500,000 to the Catholic University of America, plus endowments of a Chair of Canon Law and a Chair of Philosophy. He presented the Extension Society with a Chapel Car and a $100,000 gift. The Paulist Fathers also received $100,000. In San José, the judge purchased the sites for the Holy Family Convent, and St. Mary's Church, a national parish for German-speaking residents. He contributed generously toward construction of Holy Family Church for Italian-speaking parishioners in 1905. For St. Joseph's, of which he was a member, he was the financial force behind the $12,000 dome, a $6,000 organ and a new heating system.

Amanda O'Connor was widowed seventeen years. She carried on the O'Connor legacy of philanthropy, favoring individuals as well as sanitarium projects and area charities. Always seen in a black bonnet and a dress of black satin, taffeta or brocade, she lived in a world of her own. On the grounds she enjoyed her rose collection in the courtyard and visited the chapel regularly. She traveled in a black phaeton in her infrequent trips around the city. Her coachman lived in stylish quarters above the stables. Young San José girls like Amelia Schirle and Lillian Imhoff worked for Mrs. O'Connor as housekeepers. Lillian Imhoff, who later married cannery executive and sports librarian Fred J. Imhof, remembers her three years at the sanitarium:

"Mrs. O'Connor lived in only a couple of rooms of the house. A nurse would serve her meals. She didn't go out much. Each summer she would spend two months at a hot springs resort near St. Paul, Minnesota. I was paid twenty dollars a month and meals, a good wage in those days. Occasionally, relatives from Sacramento would visit her. She was very devoted to her husband's memory. Each Saturday morning without fail, we would take the coach to the cemetery where she would visit the grave." A niece, Mrs. J. Werry, stayed with Mrs. O'Connor in her later years. After two years as an invalid, she died on April 11, 1926, at the age of ninety.

Mrs. O'Connor's hand-in-hand communion with her husband through the years entitled her to a generous share of the tributes heaped on the O'Connor name. She could personally rejoice in the summarization of Myles P. O'Connor's life by the *San Francisco Monitor*:

"His name will never be forgotten while God and nobility are remembered; for he has planted the seeds of those better things in hearts without number."

The men's ward at O'Connor Sanitarium 50 years ago. Many "homers" —elderly persons who lived in the building permanently—still were found as late as the Twenties.

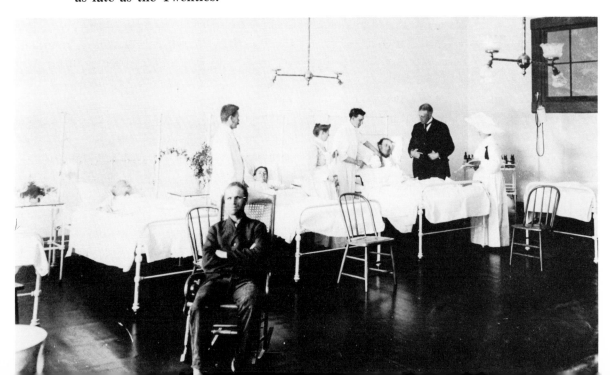

CHAPTER ELEVEN

O'Connor Hospital Yesterday, Today and Tomorrow

The Santa Clara Valley, from the orchards and berry patches of the countryside to the backyard verdure of the city, was truly a garden in the early years of the 20th century. The sylvan Santa Cruz Mountains on the west and the chameleon-like hills on the east, in seasonal rotation from tawny brown to emerald green, framed the flat valley floor. In San José, a young theatre manager named Sid Graumann was booking vaudeville acts. A singer calling himself Al Jolson readied for his stage debut. Roscoe (Fatty) Arbuckle, an ambitious lad with stars in his eyes, sold tickets at the Unique Theater on Santa Clara Street.

At 3 o'clock in the morning, insominacs at O'Connor Sanitarium could hear the clanging bells of horse-drawn lumber wagons from the Santa Cruz Mountains as they

A Daughter of Charity crosses the court-yard behind O'Connor Sanitarium in the Thirties. Much of the landscaping was planned by Mr. and Mrs. O'Connor.

rolled down dusty Stevens Creek Road. The whinny of horses and puling of hens were familiar sounds to early rising patients at the sanitarium in the country.

By 1902, it was obvious to Sister Superior Mary Agnes Gleason that the advancement of medicine demanded up-to-date facilities. She set up an operating room north of the main entrance. Instruments were sterilized in boiling water on the kitchen range in the basement, then carried upstairs. Operations were big events, numbering two and three a week and often attracting out-of-town physicians as observers. In 1906, operations had increased to a point where Sister Victorine ordered built a complete new surgical wing north of the main unit. It was here that thousands of operations were performed for almost half a century, sometimes as many as 7,000 a year.

By 1910 the sanitation complex included the main building, two wings, chapel, kitchen, laundry, power house and stables. Charles D. Blaney donated an isolation building for contagious diseases that same year. Blaney, who with his wife performed many acts of philanthropy from their Rancho Bella Vista estate in Saratoga, was California's first State Highway Commission chairman under appointment of Governor Hiram Johnson.

Sanitarium departments included x-ray, medical, obstetrical, electrotherapeutic, sur-

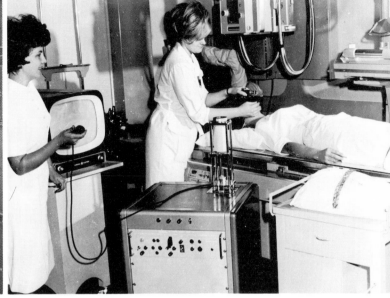

The O'Connor Sanitarium's X-ray Department (left) as it appeared in 1911. Nurses demonstrate the hospital's modern radiology facilities today (right) where more than 25,000 examinations are made annually.

gical, clinical laboratory and pharmacy. Although staff physicians were proud of the new x-ray equipment, knowledge of radiology was still superficial. There was little conception of the damaging side effects resulting from repeated exposure to the rays.

On October 25, 1909, six-year-old Mary Swartz was brought to O'Connor's with a staple lodged in her throat. Drs. Eugene A. Filipello, Mark Hopkins and E. N. Thomas and nurse Ethel Townsend tended to the patient while the child's throat was x-rayed numerous times. Miss Townsend, a granddaughter of pioneer San José physician John Townsend, and Dr. Hopkins suffered painful burns from this and other x-ray exposures.

While O'Connor's continued improvements were making it a true hospital in the most technical sense of the word, there still was a barnyard in the rear. Sister Stella Leacy took care of that. The only sister to serve twice as O'Connor superior (1921-23 and 1941-47), she found pigs, cows, chickens and rabbits roaming the 14-acre site. "When I arrived in 1921, the first thing I

did was get rid of the hogs," she recalled later. "And the Holsteins went, too." Although the sisters now had an automobile, they were faithful to their old horse which had served them so well. He was retired in 1915, but was permitted to stay on until his death in 1927.

Dr. Morgan Dillon Baker was director of the revamped x-ray department in 1923 when it was moved to the basement. Dr. Baker, San José's pioneer roentgenologist, was well known in his field and practiced 35 years in the valley until his death at the age of 59 in 1939. He was O'Connor chief of staff in 1928.

Two elevators were installed at O'Connor's in 1925. But the last major renovation in the old sanitarium occurred following Mrs. O'Connor's death when her home was remodeled into a pediatrics division on the first floor, with the sisters moving upstairs. Their old quarters were transformed into a dormitory, an infirmary, a kitchenette and bathroms. The maternity division was enlarged and remodeled the same year.

129

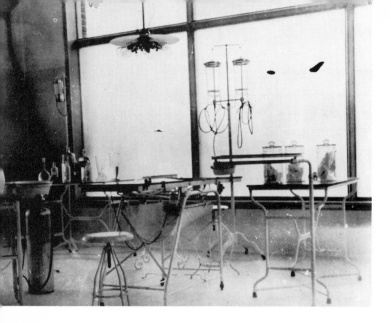

The O'Connor Sanitarium's surgical facilities (above) 50 years ago were basic and unrefined. An operation was a big event in those days, averaging 200 a year. Physicians would come from miles around in their buggies to witness a major surgery. In O'Connor Hospital's modern surgery (below), operations number more than 8,000 a year.

The sanitarium found itself with a new name, the House of Tenderness, in the Thirties. It was originated by Fremont Older, the crusading San Francisco newspaper editor whose wife was brought in dying late one night. The condition of Mrs. Older, an author and flower fancier (she planted rose bushes from 19 of California's 21 missions in San José Municipal Rose Garden), was feared hopeless by her physician. But she survived a lengthy operation and her husband, a hard-boiled newspaperman who was credited by authoress Miriam Allen Deford for coining such words as "mutt," "higher-ups," and "gangster," described in his *San Francisco Bulletin* column the hospital scene the next morning:

"At daylight I saw her. She was holding

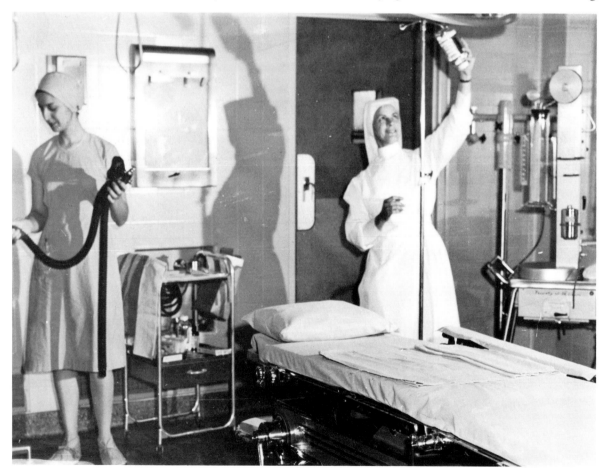

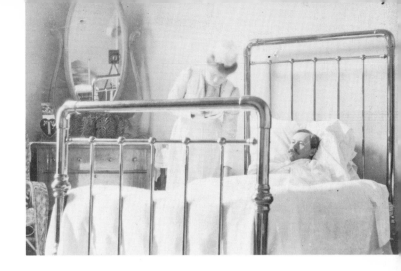

the hand of her nurse (a sister). 'She is an angel,' she whispered. 'There is nothing but tenderness here.' The sisters in their white coronets hover about like beautiful spirits from another world . . . They seem serenely happy in the life they have chosen as they flit about consoling the stricken ones. It was all as strange to me as if I had been transported to another planet. I shall never again pass O'Connor Sanitarium without a quickening of the heart beat and a thankfulness that it exists. To me, this institution is no longer the O'Connor Sanitarium. It is the House of Tenderness."

Dr. A. J. Monty, concerned over a 1930 newspaper story out of Chicago in which a hospital mixed up four mothers and their babies, instituted a system at O'Connor's to footprint each infant. The baby's footprint and the mother's fingerprint were affixed to the same record card. Previously, a baby's name was written on adhesive tape applied to its wrist, but Dr. Monty feared the tape might be washed off and lost.

The ancient vows of the Daughters of Charity to care for the poor and destitute was never more poignantly tested than during those early days of the 20th century. It was tradition in San José that a down-and-outer could always find a meal at the sanitarium. In 1911, the sisters admitted 93 "sick poor" without charge, served 3,950 meals and themselves made 48 relief visits to needy homes. Sister Dolores, her surrey piled high with groceries and clothing, was a familiar sight on San José streets. She visited the city jail regularly, chatting with the prisoners and bringing them confectionaries. She was even known to keep some of the old familiar faces supplied with pipe tobacco.

And through the Twenties and Thirties, strings of hoboes would emerge from the

An O'Connor Sanitarium nurse takes the pulse of a patient in high brass bed (above) about 1910. Oriental rugs covered the floors of high-ceilinged rooms. Today's intensive care room (below) at O'Connor Hospital is modern and functional.

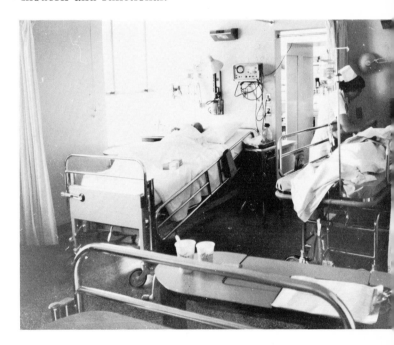

Los Gatos Creek bed and march in seried array a few blocks west to O'Connor's where a tasty meal was always available. The sisters hospitalized hundreds of financially distressed valley residents on a part-pay or free basis during the Depression. Sister Augustine Mealey directed the social relief program during the late Forties and Fifties and the Spanish-speaking poor knew they had only to come and mention her name to receive aid. Even today, the sisters still carry into the community the charity fostered by their patron, St. Vincent de Paul.

Sister Stella, from the day she banished the sanitarium's pigs and cows in 1921, took an extraordinary interest in the institution's well-being. She had a keen insight into both hospital and community needs. In 1942, when blackouts were routine in the valley and citizens took wartime precautions, Sister Stella and Chief of Staff Dr. S. V. Campisi had built a three-room gas decontamination unit on the grounds. Erected under direction of Dr. Dwight Bissell, city health officer, the area's first such unit fortunately was never needed.

It was during these war years that a groundswell of new residents began to tax the valley's medical facilities. Sister Stella saw that O'Connor's soon would have to expand if it were to meet the challenge. O'Connor Chief of Staff Dr. Leon P. Fox, Sister Superior Stella, and her successor, Sister Berenice, apprized the archbishop's office of the hospital bed crisis and O'Connor's inability to cope with it. On March 23, 1947, Archbishop John J. Mitty announced plans in a letter to Santa Clara Valley Catholic churches for a fund drive to build a new 300-bed, three-million dollar hospital on the Race Street site. O'Connor's attorney, John Burnett, confirmed the project the next day. Thus was launched a seven-year campaign that was marked by successes, failures, frustrations, and abandoned plans and renewed hopes, all of which finally crystallized in a hospital on a site and at a cost unimaginable at the beginning.

The drive opened on November 2, 1947, under the direction of newspaper publisher Patrick Peabody. The goal in

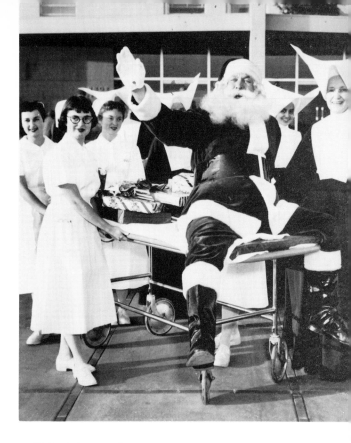

Television and movie star Ward Bond plays Santa Claus at 1954 Christmas party for O'Connor Hospital employes. Bond, a long-time friend of Hospital Administrator Sister Helen, improvises with a gurney for a sleigh and these attractive nurses for reindeer.

(Courtesy of San Jose Mercury-News)

public subscription was one millions dollars with the sisters agreeing to match that figure. The appeal mobilized an entire community, with volunteer and financial help coming from Protestants, Jews and Catholics alike. The selling points were simple. The need for the new facility was all too obvious. In O'Connor's 60-year history, records showed that 54.1 per cent of the patients had been non-Catholics. The sanitarium never had approached the community for monetary aid before.

Physicians themselves gave more than $200,000. Frank O'Connell, a Gilroy cattleman, topped individual supporters with a $30,000 gift. Emperor Hirohito's white horse was secured from Japan and exhibited to raise funds. At Bay Meadows race track, talented jockey Johnny Longden rode On Trust to victory in the O'Connor Handicap, bringing more money into the coffers. In four months, on March 11, 1948, the drive went over the top at $1,046,997. It was the largest sum ever subscribed by the public in one campaign in Santa Clara Valley. A total of 4,644 firms and individuals gave an average of $353 to achieve the goal. Still short of the three million dollar cost of the structure, Peabody said construction would begin anyway. Officials prayed additional funds would be forthcoming. A $200,000 nursing home also was planned for the Race Street site. Test borings began in December, 1948, hinting construction was about to begin. But there were no signs of construction. Segments of the community grew restless. Then, three years after the first announcement of building plans, Sister Berenice revealed O'Connor's was moving. After considerable hand wringing and egg shell tip-toeing through the mazes of governmental and business finance, the decision to erect an entirely new plant was made.

Sister Berenice and three staff presidents —Dr. Earl O. G. Schmitt (1948), Dr. Henry G. Zanger (1949) and Dr. E. D. Kilbourne Jr. (1950)—negotiated for Hill-Burton funds to help defray the costs. The Federal grant of $1,190,961 was the largest ever made to a hospital on the Pacific Coast. The government insisted on a new site, the old one along San Carlos Street having become one of the noisiest and busiest in the valley. The quest for the new site necessitated much of the secrecy adding to the delay. The 24-acre pear orchard site off Forest Avenue was purchased from V. T. McCurdy. The 1947 hospital plan was junked and a new four-story, $3,600,000 structure was announced. But the contrac-

tor's bid of $4,299,000 on May 23, 1951, reflected the skyrocketing costs of the times. Sister Berenice and chief of staff Dr. Richard T. Bigotti found themselves $909,978 short. Patrick Peabody and his campaigners were called on again. They raised part of it, the sisters borrowed more and Uncle Sam added $300,000 to his original grant.

Finally, on July 19, 1951, the construction firm of Barrett & Hilp of San Francisco broke ground. The cornerstone was laid June 12, 1953. By ingenious scheduling, only 50 patients had to be moved from the venerable old sanitarium to the E-shaped new structure that began welcoming patients on the weekend of Jan. 23-24, 1954. Sister Berenice was not there for the opening. She had been transferred to a new assignment six months previously. But Sister Stella, whose first stay at O'Connor's occurred in 1898, was one of the patients transferred to the magnificent new

Violinist Yehudi Menuhin shows O'Connor Hospital administrator Sister Helen and student nurses a ukulele grip on his priceless Stradivarius. Menuhin played a 30-minute concert in 1955 for nurses and employes in gratitude for the kindness his wife had received as a patient.

(Courtesy of San Jose Mercury-News)

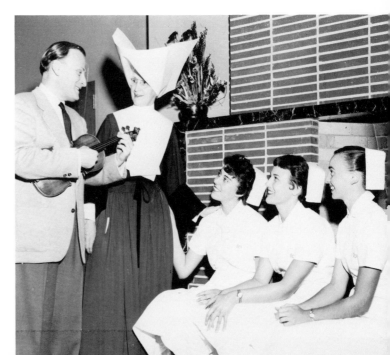

Workmen found razing the sturdily built old O'Connor Sanitarium like dismantling a battleship. Sentimental persons carted off souvenirs from the site and two Los Gatos men built their homes from the old timbers.

(Courtesy of San Jose Mercury-News)

six million dollar plant. Satisfied her long-time wish for a new hospital had been fulfilled, she died on June 13, 1954.

Sister Margaret Callahan, the administrator, and Chief of Staff Dr. Helen Hardenbergh dutifully greeted the first arrivals at the new facility. The honor of being the first patient went to six-year-old Howard Walter, son of Mr. and Mrs. John Walter of San José. Suffering from a ruptured appendix, he recovered in a short time. A rustle of white garments and a flutter of feathers accompanied the arrival of the first stork. He brought in baby Linda, the six-pound four-ounce daughter of Mr. and Mrs. John S. Luiz of Sunnyvale. The occasion was marked by the cancelling of all hospital charges for this first little visitor.

The old 14-acre site was sold for $400,-000 in November, 1954, for construction of a new Sears store. The price was $100,-000 more than it cost Myles P. O'Connor to build the entire sanitarium 65 years previously. New administrator Sister

Helen McMahon had hoped she could spend the money to build a convent for the sisters, who were using a 30-bed section of the hospital as a residence. But she decided to apply it toward the substantial mortgage. The swishing lead ball of wreckers sent the last brick wall of the old O'Connor's crashing to the ground in May, 1955, a feat of destruction that even the 1906 earthquake could not accomplish.

Wrecking crews found that razing the old sanitarium was like trying to dismantle a battleship with a cub scout troop. In some places, the walls were 20-brick thick. One man bought all the bricks and he was believed to have made a small fortune reselling them. Grant H. Rogers and Hector H. Aiken of Los Gatos purchased some of the old timbers and used them to build their own homes. Aiken transformed the weathered granite front steps of the sanitarium into an entranceway for his residence.

"Some of the big beams were marked with the name of the ship that had carried them down here from the Pacific Northwest," Rogers remembers. "It took me four months, working by a lantern at night, just to pull out the old square nails. I almost lost the friendship of one of my neighbors. I had piled the lumber on an empty lot and there were remarks that ether was smelling up the neighborhood."

Others with a sentimental affection for the venerable sanitatium combed it for souvenirs. A San José wood carver transformed a piece of redwood bannister into a beautiful madonna.

San José merchant John McEnery recollected that not all the sanitarium's valuable articles were saved.

"When the wreckers started on the old building," he said, "it occurred to me that the plaque on the St. Matthew's Chapel might not have been retrieved. I asked Sister Helen, the new administrator, and she said she didn't know. We both rushed over to the old property, but were too late. Someone had taken it. Myles O'Connor had had

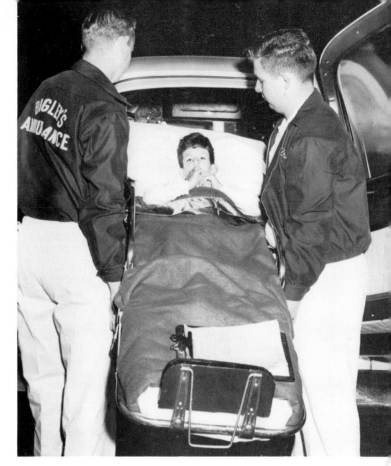

Howard Walter, then six years old, was the first patient registered at O'Connor Hospital when it opened in January, 1954. Howard recovered after treatment for a ruptured appendix.

(Courtesy of San Jose Mercury-News)

The first baby born in the new O'Connor Hospital was six-pound, four-ounce Linda Luiz in January, 1954. Sister Irene and nurse Elizabeth Mulcahy congratulate the parents, Mr. and Mrs. John S. Luiz.

(Courtesy of San Jose Mercury-News)

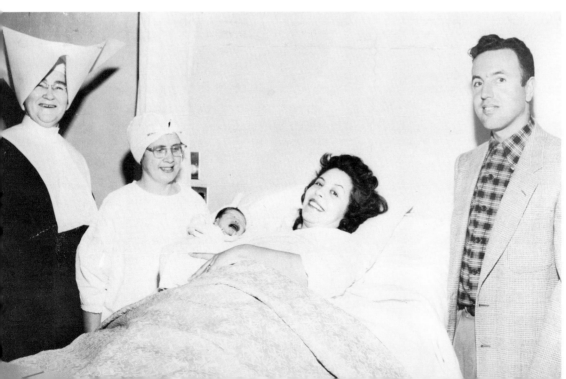

135

it put up in his brother's memory. The plaque was solid gold. It must have been worth $1,800 to $2,000."

O'Connor's coasted through the pre-World War I years averaging 1,000 patients a year. When the admissions shot to 2,440 in the influenza year of 1918, the sanitarium staff was overwhelmed. Expanded facilities enabled the institution to average about 2,400 patients a year through the Twenties, and a little below that during the Depression when hospitals from coast to coast were running at 55 per cent admission capacity because of economic conditions. In the old days, a patient's stay averaged two weeks. But by 1946, a burgeoning valley population called for a faster turnover to even approach the demand for hospital services. The 10,193 admissions at O'Connor's in 1946 was a fiat that led to the campaign for a new building. But little did the sisters and doctors realize that the strain on their facilities would continue. They sent up a hurried SOS after 1957 when the 254-bed hospital counted 19,888 admissions. This figure meant for its size O'Connor's had registered more patients than any other hospital in the United States, its territories or Canada. The employe payroll jumped a quarter of a million dollars in one year. One out of every six patients was being turned away.

Many patients spent their entire stay on a gurney in the hallway. Sister Superior Helen McMahon and chiefs of staff Dr. Richard T. Bigotti (1957) and Dr. Carl O. Carlson (1958) called on Patrick Peabody to marshal his workers for the third time. They raised most of their goal of $300,000, enabling the sisters to plan for their own residence and to increase bed capacity by 13 per cent through the freeing

Sister Roberta, O'Connor Hospital administrator since 1959. She and her staff currently are planning a three million dollar expansion program for the hospital.

of a 30-bed section the sisters had used as a living area.

The late Fifties and early Sixties brought an influx of new hospitals to the valley, including the $6 million Alexian Brothers institution built on land donated by public-spirited Mildred Overfelt. Descendent of a pioneer family, Miss Overfelt bequeathed 17 acres as a memorial to her brother Jackson. It is the first Alexian Brothers hospital in the 500-year history of the order caring for all members of the family.

Since the early years when Myles O'Connor arranged for Bishop Keane, first president of Catholic University, to spend summer rests at the sanitarium, the institution has seen many a renowned figure pass through its portals.

Violin virtuoso Yehudi Menuhin played a 30-minute program of Bach for 125 O'Connor staff members in 1955 to say "thank you" for the kind treatment his wife had received as a patient. "It seems like the natural thing to do," he smiled halfway through the program. "I am apparently the only violinist in the hospital well enough to play." Actor Ward Bond, actress June Haver and the tandem entertainers, Edgar Bergen and Charlie McCarthy, all performed for nurses and patients. Governor Goodwin J. Knight inspected the new facility on October 25, 1954. Bing Crosby was in a distraught frame of mind

while he waited in the hospital lobby in 1954 for word of his son, Gary. The younger Crosby escaped serious injury in a Sunnyvale auto accident.

Hospital employes normally pay little heed to noises such as caterwauling sirens, but they did a double take in 1956 when they heard the whirr of a helicopter in the front parking lot. It was carrying a wounded Turlock deer hunter who had been transported from the Mt. Hamilton Range.

The nursing school is not the only section of the hospital plant that embraces an academic atmosphere. In 1951, Dr. Leslie Grams started a one-year training program for medical technologists. A five-year program for resident pathologists also was

The O'Connor Hospital Chapel, as seen in this architect's drawing, opened in November, 1965. It completed the 1953 master plan for the hospital plant.

CHAPEL FOR O'CONNOR HOSPITAL
SAN JOSE · CALIFORNIA
FRANK W. TRABUCCO · ARCHITECT
A.I.A.
SAN FRANCISCO

instituted. Graduates hold positions in leading hospitals throughout the United States and Canada.

The Department of Radiology, from its beginnings in the old sanitarium, grew steadily to where it was conducting more than 25,000 examinations a year in the Sixties. Some 60 per cent of the total were out-patients. Department head Dr. Thomas N. Foster first joined the radiology staff in 1944 in the sanitarium basement when it was necessary to duck overhanging pipes to cross the room. He was O'Connor staff president in 1955.

The O'Connor Hospital Auxiliary was formed in 1952 as an aid to the Daughters of Charity in the institution's operations. The volunteer organization, through its many projects, has raised more than $100,-000 which was turned back into the hospital for new equipment and furnishings. The taking of baby pictures, the gift shop and the mobile magazine stands have been among the most successful programs.

The master plan concept of the new O'Connor's was completed in December, 1965, with the opening of the hospital's chapel. Seating 100 persons, the chapel represented an investment of $250,000.

As was the case in the 1890's when O'Connor Sanitarium served in effect as a San José municipal hospital, the demand for the most modern facilities has been constant with the growth of the community.

To keep O'Connor in the forefront as one of California's leading medical institutions, administrator Sister Roberta, and her assistant, Sister Fidelis, worked closely in the mid-Sixties with medical staff members Drs. J. Frederic Snyder, Frank Giansiracusa, Daniel G. Vaughan, Thomas Kenter and William L. Molineux to formulate plans for a three million dollar expansion program.

The project, scheduled to begin in 1966 and take eighteen months to complete, will take shape as an addition on the hospital's southwest side. It will embrace up-to-date x-ray, laboratory and physical medicine facilities, recovery rooms, an intensive care unit and a new administration office.

Born in the horse and buggy era, O'Connor Hospital entered the Space Age with the same vision and high ideals that characterized its founder when he struck out for the setting sun and an uncertain future on that spring morning of 1849.

The never-ending pursuit of new means to relieve the suffering carries on the spirit of compassion and philanthropy that marked the life of Myles Poore O'Connor.

For his was the creed delineated by the poet, Joaquin Miller:

"O God! How poor a man may be
With nothing in this world but gold!"

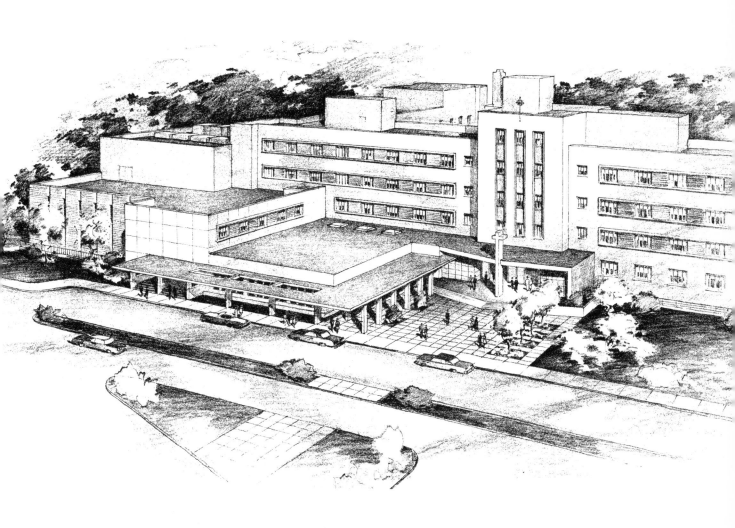

Artist's sketch of new O'Connor Hospital expansion program. Scheduled for completion in 1968, it will include x-ray, laboratory and physical medicine facilities, an intensive care unit and a new administration office.

Acknowledgements

Any historian or biographer necessarily must rely on libraries and people for most of his material.

I am grateful to Clyde Arbuckle, director of the San José City Museum, and Joseph B. Ridder, publisher of the *San José Mercury-News*, for making their files available at both regular and odd hours. Historian Arbuckle's personal knowledge of places and events in Santa Clara Valley's past and present was invaluable.

Other historians were of great assistance. They include Dr. John Barr Tompkins, Bancroft Library, University of California; Edwin H. Carpenter and Robert O. Dongan, Huntington Library, San Marino, California; Sister Regina, archivist, Marillac Provincial House of the Daughters of Charity of St. Vincent de Paul, St. Louis, Missouri; Sister Josephine, archivist, Provincial House, Emmitsburg, Maryland; Sister Columba, vice president of academic affairs, Trinity College, Washington, D.C.; Thomas Vaughan, Director, Oregon Historical Society, and the staffs of the San José City and Santa Clara County Libraries.

A thesis by Sister Helen Cecelia, of the Sisters of Notre Dame de Namur, on the life of Myles O'Connor was an important source. Sister Joan Marie, of the College of Notre Dame, graciously offered the O'Connor diaries for the author's perusal.

I am indebted to the Rev. Robert Duryea, chaplain of O'Connor Hospital, whose photographic skills were instrumental in compiling the pictorial sections of the book. I wish it were possible to thank publicly all the persons who aided in this project. Without attempting to qualify the contributions of these benefactors, I want to thank Dr. E. Paul Cook, Dr. C. Kelly Canelo, Mrs. Gerard Kettman, Judge Marshall Hall, Dr. William Molineux, Sister Fidelis, Sister Antoine, Dr. Jack Lange, Dr. James Ransom, Roger Clarke, Anton F. Peterson, Mrs. Harriet Mathews, Sister Constance, Mrs. Julie Kenney, Harry Hind, Joseph F. Donovan, Dr. R. Morton Manson, Don L. Lee, Rosellen Palm, Samuel S. Virts, Paige Abbott, Theron Fox and the Rev. John J. McGloin, S.J.

Dr. Daniel G. Vaughan offered technical assistance and aid in manuscript preparation. Without his inspiration and enthusiasm, this book never would have been written.

I also wish to thank my wife, Gerry, for the book's title and her continuous encouragement and my daughters, Jane and Susan, for patience beyond their years.

Daniel D. Hruby

San José, California
November 16, 1965

Bibliography

Bancroft, Hubert Howe, *History of California*, The History Company, San Francisco, 1888.

Bari, Valeska, *The Course of Empire*, Coward-McCann, Inc., New York, 1931.

Bernheim, Bertram M., *The Story of Johns Hopkins*, Whittlesey House, New York, 1948.

Billington, Ray Allen, *The Far Western Frontier*, Harper & Brothers, New York, 1956.

Bronson, William, *The Earth Shook—The Sky Burned*, Doubleday, Garden City, N.Y., 1959.

Britt, Albert, *Toward the Western Ocean*, Barre Publishing Co., Barre, Mass., 1963.

——————————, California—*A Guide to the Golden State*, American Guide Series, Hastings House Publishers, New York, 1939.

Dana, Julian, *The Sacramento, River of Gold*, Rinehart & Company, New York, 1939.

DeFord, Miriam Allen, *They Were San Franciscans*, The Caxton Printers, Ltd., Caldwell, Ida., 1947.

Dodge, Bertha S., *The Story of Nursing*, Little, Brown and Company, Boston, 1954.

Drury, Aubrey, *California, An Intimate Guide*, Harper & Brothers, New York, 1935.

Foote, Horace S., *Pen Pictures from the Garden of the World, Santa Clara County, California,* The Lewis Publishing Co., Chicago, 1888.

Gilbert, Benjamin F., *Pioneers for One Hundred Years — San Jose State College, 1857-1957,* San Jose, Calif., 1957.

Hall, Frederic, *The History of San Jose and Surroundings, With Biographical Sketches of Early Settlers,* J. W. Stacey, San Francisco, 1871.

Hoehling, A. A., *The Great Epidemic*, Boston, Little, Brown and Company, 1961.

Hogan and German, *The San Francisco Chronicle Reader*, McGraw-Hill Book Publishing, Inc., New York, 1962.

Holbrook, Stewart H., *The Golden Age of Quackery*, The MacMillan Company, New York, 1959.

Hoover and Rensch, *Historic Spots in California*, Stanford University Press, 1948.

Hulbert, Archer Butler, *Forty-Niners*, Little, Brown & Company, Boston, 1931.

Hunt, Rockwell D., *Personal Sketches of California Pioneers I Have Known*, University of the Pacific, Stockton, Calif., 1952.

Jackson, Joseph Henry, *Anybody's Gold*, Appleton, New York, 1941.

Kavanagh, D. J. (S.J.), *The Holy Family Sisters of San Francisco,* Gilmartin Co., San Francisco, 1922.

Kennedy, Helen, *Vignettes of the Gardens*, San Francisco Garden Club, San Francisco, 1938.

Lyman, George D., *The Scalpel Under Three Flags in California*, California Historical Society, San Francisco, 1925.

MacEachern, Malcolm T., *Hospital Organization & Management*, Physicians' Records, Chicago, 1951.

McGlashan, C. F., *History of the Donner Party*, Stanford University Press, 1940.

Morgan, Dale L., *The Humboldt, Highroad of the West*, Rinehart & Company, New York, 1943.

Munro-Fraser, J. P., *History of Santa Clara County*, Alley, Bowen & Co., San Francisco, 1881.

Nourse, Alan E., *So You Want to be a Nurse*, Harper & Brothers, New York, 1961.

Olmsted, R. R., *Scenes of Wonder & Curiosity From Hutchings' California Magazine*, Howell-North, Berkeley, Calif., 1962.

Nunis, Doyce A., *Josiah Belden, 1841 Overland Pioneer — His Memoirs and Early Letters*, The Talisman Press, Georgetown, Calif., 1962.

Paden, Irene D., *Wake of the Prairie Schooner*, The MacMillan Company, New York, 1943.

Paul, Rodman W., *Mining Frontiers of the Far West*, Holt, Rinehart and Winston, New York, 1963.

Piercy, Frederick Hawkins, *Route from Liverpool to Salt Lake Valley, Illustrated with Steel Engravings and Wood Cuts from Sketches Made by Frederick Piercy*, Edited by James Linforth, Liverpool, 1855.

Read and Gaines, *Gold Rush*, Columbia University Press, New York, 1949.

Rice, Bertha, *Builders of Our Valley*, 1957.

Richardson, Robert G., *The Surgeon's Tale*, Charles Scribner's Sons, New York, 1958.

Russell, Hubert D., *Complete Story of the San Francisco Horror*, 1906.

Sawyer, Eugene T., *History of Santa Clara County*, Historic Record Company, Los Angeles, Calif., 1922.

Shinn, Charles Howard, *Mining Camps*, Alfred A. Knopf, New York, 1948.

——————, *History of Santa Clara County and Its Resources* (Sunshine, fruit and flowers), 1895.

Spearman, Arthur Dunning, (S.J.), *The Five Franciscan Churches of Mission Santa Clara*, The National Press, Palo Alto, Calif.

Stewart, George R., *Donner Pass and Those Who Crossed It*, Lone Book Company, Menlo Park, Calif., 1959.

Stewart, George R., *Ordeal by Hunger*, The Riverside Press, Cambridge, Mass., 1936.
Sutherland, Monica, *The Damndest Finest Ruins*, Coward-McCann Inc., New York, 1959.

Taylor, Bayard, *Eldorado*, Putnam, New York, 1894.

Thorwald, Jurgen, *The Triumph of Surgery*, Pantheon Books Inc., New York, 1957.

Tyler, Sidney, *San Francisco's Great Disaster*, P. W. Zeigler Co., Philadelphia, Pa., 1906.

Walker, Kenneth, *The Story of Medicine*, Oxford University Press, New York, 1955.

Wellman, Paul I., *Gold in California*, The Riverside Press, Cambridge, Mass., 1958.

Wells, Evelyn, and Peterson, Harry C., *The '49ers*, Doubleday & Company, Garden City, N.Y., 1949.

Williams, Greer, *Virus Hunters*, Alfred A. Knopf, New York, 1959.

Index

147

148